# CAST A COLD EYE

## Marjorie Eccles

Constable · London

First published in Great Britain 1999
by Constable & Company Ltd.
3 The Lanchesters, 162 Fulham Palace Road,
London W6 9ER

ISBN 0 094 79830 3

Printed and bound in Great Britain by
MPG Books Ltd, Bodmin

A CIP catalogue record for this book
is available from the British Library

# Cast a Cold Eye

*Cast a Cold Eye*

# CHAPTER 1

The party was still in full swing, but it had been over for a long time as far as the pair from the *Advertiser* was concerned, Matt could see.

The young reporter, bored out of his mind, accepted his third glass of champagne, or maybe his fourth, shot his cuff to look at his watch yet again, and rolled up his eyes at the photographer.

Well, it wouldn't be his kind of party, would it? No music, no dancing. Not even outside in the spacious gardens as it would have been a few weeks earlier, before October set in. Instead, polite chat and restrained laughter in the elegant surroundings of the Lethbridge drawing room here at Brome House, all rich, deep colours, dark panelling and antique furniture. Not his scene at all. Experience told Matt what it felt like to wait like this, wishing your host would get on with the knitting—the speeches, the toasts, whatever—so that you could get your story and get the hell out of it, and back to civilisation. In this case, on the road from Brome to Lavenstock. Matt grinned in sympathy, and then, as Caroline came up to him, he forgot all about the pair.

Clive Lethbridge wasn't anywhere near ready yet to wind up his party. He was very obviously enjoying it, basking in the congratulations which fell upon him like manna as he circulated among one group and another. Expansive, flushed with the triumph of his success, having his hand pumped and his back slapped, Clive was a man on the crest of a wave.

A telephone rang somewhere in the recesses of the house, and presently Clive's secretary, a mousy girl with round, thick-lensed spectacles, sought him out, catching him between groups. Briefly, as she spoke to him, Clive stood very still. Then with his heavy, purposeful stride, he left the room.

It was some time before he came back, and it was perhaps only his wife, Caroline—and Matt, who was as usual watching her reactions—who noticed the difference in him.

"Excuse me a minute, Matt." Pushing back the smooth wing of dark hair that fell across her cheek, giving Matt a glimpse of her slow, sweet smile, Caroline left him with only the faint drift of her elusive scent and the touch of cool fingers on his wrist. He watched her walk, graceful and unhurried, her dress a drift of soft dove colour, to the table by the window, where Clive was pouring himself a stiff scotch, downing it in one go and then pouring another.

Matt caught a sideways view of their reflections in the dark window. Standing beside Clive, completing the picture of the pair they presented to the world, Caroline's petite slenderness was a piquant contrast to Clive's big, heavyset frame. An unusual, intriguing couple. With a sharp twist of irony Matt thought, not for the first time, that the coarse-grained Lethbridge had at least shown a redeeming streak of sensitivity in choosing Caroline for a wife. Her money, of course, could not have been a disadvantage, either.

All right, one had to respect the man, professionally at any rate. He was a demon for work and extremely competent—in a fairly run-of-the-mill way, yet with occasional flashes of something like inspiration, now flowered into the astonishing, soaring vision personified in the architectural model set on the table in the centre of the room, together with the photographs of its final realisation, humbling Matt as he looked at them yet again. What standards was a man judged by, after all?

With more force than was necessary, Matt ground out the stub of the cigarette he shouldn't have been smoking. If he'd any sense, he would pack the job in, shake the dust off his feet here and now, tell Conti that he'd either have to find another architect than Clive to collaborate on the production of the book, or find another writer. But he knew he was only making noises. It was too late; he had long since gone beyond the point of no return.

Often lately, in the sleepless reaches of the night, Matt regretted having allowed Conti to persuade him into accepting the commission, but he was well aware that, given the chance again, he'd make the same decision. The work had brought him into touch with Caroline, who, besides being Clive's wife, worked as a publisher's reader for Conti. And for the second time in a year, he found his life and its direction turned upside down.

Clive, whatever his other faults, had been only a moderate drinker since his doctor had told him to lay off if he wanted to keep his weight and his blood pressure down, and he'd already consumed what he regarded as his quota. Caroline felt a prickle of unease as she saw the speed with which he now drank this, then another whisky. He was drinking automatically, staring at his own distorted reflection in the rain-spattered lattice of the darkened window behind the drinks table, his face drained of its ruddy glow of self-congratulation. That telephone call. Maybe it wasn't his reflection he was staring at; maybe he was looking beyond the darkness, to the house on the slope of the far side of the valley, where the Dymonds lived.

"Clive? What's wrong?"

He broke his stare, turning to face her. "What do you mean, wrong?" His voice would have sounded normal to anyone else, but she was too used to his moods not to notice the edge to it, to know that his euphoria had left him. A prominent vein pulsed in his temple, as it always did when he was upset, a dead giveaway. A storm signal for rough weather ahead.

She took a steadying breath. "I meant the phone call. Was it another one of—of *those?* You look . . ." "Desperate" was the word, but not to be used now, with controlled violence just below the surface of his calm.

"It's nothing," he replied with an effort. "I've just had enough of this bloody lot, that's all." He half turned as he spoke, pinning a social smile on to his face, and nodding to someone who caught his eye. "Clear them out, Caro."

It was a command rather than a request, and she bit her lip at the arbitrary tone but deliberately stifled her resentment.

"All right, but you *are* supposed to be celebrating, don't forget. People aren't expecting to go just yet. And Harry's waiting to say a few words."

"Oh God, yes, Harry." His strong, blunt fingers had tightened round his glass until the knuckles were white. "Harry, by all means. Tell him to get on with it, then."

Harry Waring, Clive's senior partner, smooth and late-fifty-ish, rosy with good living, was standing beside the table that held the model, cigar in one hand, glass in the other, having just escaped Clive's new secretary. He took a revivifying sip. God, but she was hard work, no conversation, that one, that Susan—no, Sylvia, Sylvia Johnson, never could remember her name. Difficult to remember *her*, sometimes—a personality as drab as that potato-coloured dress which did even less for her than her usual dreary skirts and jumpers.

Thoughtfully, he contemplated the model. "Astonishing, isn't it?" he remarked to Matt, who had just joined him.

Astonishing. The very word Matt himself had chosen earlier. "Sure," he agreed, though not altogether certain what Waring had intended by the word. Astonishing as an architectural concept, or merely astonishing for Clive Lethbridge?

Waring said suddenly, "I'd like a word, Royston. Can we fix a time?"

Matt nodded, surprised. "I shall be away for the next week, but when I get back I'll give you a ring. Will that do?"

"Yes, do that if you would. Ah, Caroline." At the sound of her low, slightly husky voice, Harry turned affectionately towards Caroline, who was in his opinion everything a woman should be—pretty and feminine, socially adept, clever, too. Just the right wife for a man in Clive's position—though

Clive needed a kick up the pants for how he treated her sometimes.

Caroline smiled at him, the luminous blue of her eyes lighting the habitual gravity of her expression. "Are you ready, Harry?"

Harry had expected, indeed asked for, the opportunity to make a small speech on this occasion, and he would perform with his usual urbanity, Caroline knew, so that when he began she was surprised that it was hesitantly, without his usual fluent composure. After a moment or two, however, he was into his stride, making a polished and graceful performance of it, conceding the honours for the success that had lately fallen on to the firm justly to Clive's brilliant, award-winning design, following its success in a world-wide competition.

There were handclaps for him as well as Clive when he paused appropriately so that Clive, who had by now taken a grip on himself, could acknowledge the accolade, and murmur something deprecating about it all being a team effort. Harry resumed, smiling. Yet Caroline, accustomed to his witty and humorous deliveries, again detected something a trifle forced, almost as if, she thought, he were trying to convince himself as well as his audience of the value of the splendid design, which of course was nonsense, an aberration on her part; no one else appeared to have noticed. Her eyes unconsciously searched the room for Matt, but if she had expected to be able to read on his face confirmation of what he was thinking, she was disappointed.

He was leaning negligently against the wall, a little apart from the rest, a tall, rangy man with a fading tan, straight, grey-threaded fair hair and contrastingly marked dark brows. A strong, mature face, experienced and knowledgeable. He was thirty-six and looked older, and there was a wry quality about him, a way of looking at himself as well as others, that might just, one day, turn to cynicism. At that moment, as if at some prearranged signal, he turned his head and their eyes met, and things carefully unspoken between them ever since they had been introduced were suddenly and silently said.

Caroline felt a wave of actual faintness. It was as though some support to which she had been desperately trying to cling for weeks had given way, and she was adrift, fighting breathlessly against a tide that was inevitably going to carry her away, into forbidden waters. Desperately, with an almost physical effort, she forced herself and her attention back to what was going on.

Harry had finally finished. Glasses were being raised, the photographer's bulbs flashing. The young reporter's usually laboured shorthand flowed under the influence of the champagne. Caroline was asked to pose with Clive for a photograph which would be on the front page of next week's *Advertiser*. Clive was asked for a quote. And then the party was really over.

# CHAPTER 2

Clive was in the habit of working at home one day per week, more if he happened to be pressed. It gave him personal space, time to catch up on the backlog of correspondence which accumulated during the week, and to review his plans without constant interruption. There was peace here, unlike his main offices in the centre of Birmingham, where everyone was on top of everyone else and there was no room to swing a cat. He had to have this mid-week change of gear; he *needed* it —especially today, the morning after the celebration party.

For by God, he thought savagely, simmering with controlled rage as he remembered yet again, no slimy-tongued anonymous telephone caller was going to mess up his life! He'd managed so far to ignore the insinuations and threats— well, let them get on with it and see how far they were prepared to go. Nobody was better at brinksmanship than he was. He'd had plenty of practice.

So. He sat quite still for a moment, taking a deliberate hold on himself, then opened his diary, without which he swore he couldn't function. His secretary noted down his appointments and sometimes also reminders of Caroline's social commitments so that they shouldn't clash. He had the habit of using the book almost like a scratch pad, jotting down the odd thought or calculation, sometimes making a quick sketch as an idea occurred to him, as well as making his own notes of things to be done each day. On principle, he always made this list longer than he could reasonably be expected to accomplish . . . yet rarely was it left unfinished at the end of the day. It was his way of driving himself, of going that bit further and therefore getting one up on the next man, which was, he figured, the way any thrusting, successful man should operate.

At length, he shut the book with a decisive snap and leaned back in his chair.

He saw with satisfaction that today the weather at least was in league with him, the morning very warm for early October, after the previous day's rain. There were still roses on the bushes outside the open french window, the perfume drifting in. MacAllister would see Brome House at its best, and not need too much persuasion to put his money into financing the project. Because now, *now* was the time to do it, to approach MacAllister with this latest success behind him. His gaze rested on the Svensen Centre model, now standing on a small table beside the window, and he smiled.

Situated out here, midway between Lavenstock and Birmingham, the location of Brome House was convenient, the setting idyllic. He had cultivated the habit of bringing business associates and prospective clients here, so that they could meet and discuss their business in a leisurely manner. A walk round the garden, drinks on the terrace, lunch afterwards in the gracious dining room—no need to take anyone out to lunch when Caroline, with the help of Janice Wharton, could provide better food than any local restaurant, and act as hostess at the same time. It was all part of the softening up process, which almost always worked.

Clive smiled again, hitched his chair forward and began work on a pile of routine papers, but his mind still circled round his cherished plan. She would come round, he told himself—he'd find a way to *make* her see his point of view. He was confident of his ability to find some means of putting pressure on her, making her agree to do as he wished. He fully intended anyway, Caroline or no Caroline, one way or another, to go ahead, but it would be easier with her support.

The plan, like a rich fruit-cake, had improved with keeping. He would do a first-class conversion job on Brome House here, turning the whole place into a set of prestigious offices —without, of course, spoiling the leisured country-house atmosphere. Clients liked that sort of thing—and the conversion would be an advertisement in itself. He and Caroline and Pippa would then move to the new house he planned to build on the site he had acquired lower down the valley. It was time Caroline's ideas were changed; it was ridiculous and outmoded these days to think of the three of them rattling around in a house this size, just because her family had inhabited it for generations. A pity the house was still in his wife's name; it had been the only thing he hadn't been able to persuade her to make over when her father's estate had been settled. Caroline could be very stubborn about some things.

He could hear Sylvia Johnson already moving about in the room next door, which she used as an office. It was only twenty to nine, twenty minutes before her starting time. Sylvia, too, worked here on Clive's non-city days, but she was so unobtrusive she never got in the way, and so capable he was beginning to wonder after only six weeks how he had ever doubted anyone could replace Amanda, that hitherto irreplaceable paragon of efficiency.

He reached for a blue file marked "Oddings Cottage." As he did so, the stutter of a motorbike starting up broke the silence of the morning, then roared away.

Clive sprang up and leaped through the open french windows, shading his eyes against the bright sunlight as he reached the gravel drive outside, which completely encircled the house. He was just in time to see the bike disappearing through the main gates. Without stopping to think, he charged across the lawn towards the lodge.

The back door was open. A young woman was standing by the scullery door, taking an overall from a peg.

"Where's Terry gone?" Clive demanded, stepping in uninvited, panting only slightly from his sprint. Though heavily built, a daily stint of jogging was part of his programme for keeping himself fit.

The woman spun round, paused when she saw who it was and what mood he was in, then answered calmly, beginning to roll up the overall, "Up to the university, Mr. Lethbridge. He has a seminar this morning."

"Seminar? Why didn't he tell me that yesterday? I told him then I should want him to mow the lawns if it was fine."

Janice Wharton tucked a strand of escaping hair more firmly behind her ears, a neat, brown-haired woman in her late twenties or early thirties. "I expect he forgot. It was only Saturday when he did them, wasn't it? His usual day."

"He's not damn well paid to forget! And whether he cut them then or not's immaterial. When I say I want something done, I want it done. All that rain's made the grass shoot up, and I particularly wanted the grounds to look their best to-day. He knew that—why the hell didn't he tell me yesterday he wouldn't be here?" Clive demanded, thrusting a pugnacious face close to hers, the prominent vein throbbing in his temple.

You know very well why, Janice thought, endeavouring to step unobtrusively back. If Terry *had* mentioned the seminar, Clive would have kicked up an almighty fuss, no doubt about that. All right, in the end he would probably have conceded the point because, to give him his due, he never went back on his word, and he'd promised when they came here that Terry could run his studies alongside the job—but the concession wouldn't have been given before he'd left Terry abject and humiliated. And humiliation wasn't something her husband swallowed easily. He'd learned to keep more of a rein on his temper lately, but he'd only stand so much.

Janice's hands were clenched into fists at her side. She wished fervently that Terry would at least try to be diplomatic with Clive—why wouldn't he see that he *mustn't* throw away this chance which had been given them like another life?

It was still something so wonderful she couldn't quite believe it, an opportunity for Terry to get himself qualified for a decent job, to work for a degree, and at the same time have somewhere as incredible as this to live.

"I'll see if I can find time to do the grass," she told Clive.

After all, it was only time that it took. There wasn't much effort needed. You sat on the mower seat and steered the machine round, and the motor did the rest. She'd done it before once or twice, when Terry had an essay due.

"Mrs. Lethbridge will need your help in the house this morning," Clive returned shortly, suddenly coldly formal. "Do I have to remind you that's what we employ you for?"

Quick colour stained Janice's cheeks, but all she said was, "We're well ahead with preparations for the lunch, and if I hurry with the cleaning, I'll get through." She reached for the overall and tucked it under her arm.

He said nastily, "I sometimes wonder whose benefit this arrangement we have is for," and left her without another word.

Janice glanced at the clock, saw she still had a few minutes in hand and took the time to get herself together. She found she was shivering and stood by the sink, her arms crossed, holding herself tight, looking round at every detail of the bright kitchen.

This little house, Brome Lodge, was part of the remuneration for their husband-and-wife services as home help and handyman in the house and garden. She was so proud of it; they had made it so nice, she and Terry, painting and papering and doing up the old furniture Caroline had found for them in the attics of the big house—really good stuff, some of it had turned out to be. After the appalling years of trying to bring up two children in terrible rented rooms, or even squats, it was very nearly paradise to her. There wasn't much she wouldn't do to keep it.

Meanwhile, letting Clive Lethbridge's barbs get under her skin was a luxury she couldn't afford. She had better get on if she wanted to get that grass cut before that client of his arrived. Locking the door and pocketing the key of her little kingdom, she began to walk up to the house and thought, as she did every day of her life, I wonder what he'd do if he *knew*.

A few minutes ahead of her Clive, as he went back, again taking the short cut across the unmown lawn, debated whether he shouldn't get rid of the Whartons. It had been a mistake to let Caroline persuade him with a hard-luck story when old Ganson had died and the lodge had become vacant. He wasn't averse to being regarded as a benefactor, and Janice, according to Caroline, had become indispensable, but Terry, besides being unreliable, wasn't much cop, not as a gardener anyway. He did what he was told to do—when he felt like it—but he was no substitute for Ganson. It was only the fact that he was extremely handy with the cars and odd jobs around the house that had saved him so far. All the same, he was also employed to cut the lawns, and cut them he had not. Still fuming, Clive went through the french windows into his study.

Sylvia had put the post on his desk while he had been out, unopened. Mail that came here was usually of a personal nature; anything else waited at the office until the following day, unless it was urgent, when he would be contacted. He had picked the pile up and was beginning to throw out the unsolicited junk when Sylvia walked in, drawing back in a startled manner when she saw him.

"Oh, excuse me! I didn't hear you come back in."

"Did you want something?" He spoke curtly; it would take some time for him to recover his composure.

"Oh well, only that file, with those notes of Matt Royston's you promised to check. I put it out yesterday for you to bring over; it needs tidying up."

He gestured towards his briefcase, not raising his eyes, putting an electricity bill to one side. She took the file out of the briefcase, made for the door and paused. "Mr. Lethbridge?"

"Yes?"

"There's something I'd like to have a word with you about —but it doesn't matter, it can wait," she added hastily as she watched him pick up another envelope and draw in a sharp, audible breath.

"Yes, later," he said roughly, not looking at her.

She didn't move for a moment, still watching him. "When you can spare a moment," she said at last, and went out so silently he never heard her.

Clive knew what he ought to do with the thing. Tear it into bits and flush it down the loo, as he had with the others. But just for a moment, he was scared. Frightened as he hadn't been since he was a kid, waiting for the results of the exam that could take him away from the aunt who had brought him up, and the stuffy respectability of working-class Nottingham, never to return.

Then the model caught his eye again, reassuring him.

The whole project had been envisaged and financed by a health-conscious Norwegian millionaire. Having recently visited Epidaurus, he had returned home fired with the rediscovered beliefs of ancient Greece, that the mind and body are so interdependent it is futile to treat one without the other, determined to reproduce another healing centre such as Epidaurus, though better, in Norway. The brief for the competition thus launched had included a hospital, theatre, library, and a gallery to house the millionaire's art collection. Peace and tranquility were paramount requirements; music, books and theatre were to be freely available, patients would be surrounded by paintings and sculpture, and other works of art, inside and outdoors. The whole—view, ambience, art treasures—was calculated to free the mind so that the body could be treated, or vice-versa. To be, in the jargon, a total and enriching experience.

The basic design was good—all right, outstanding, a complex of glass and steel so radical there'd been doubts about its viability—but the brilliance lay in the use to which it had been adapted, in the marriage of the site with the buildings themselves, in producing a solution so perfect to the requirements. Chosen from hundreds submitted from around the world, now finished and in use, it was set in the mountains, amongst bracing air and the dappled shade of light woodland, with breathtaking views from the windows. It was to be known as the Svensen Centre.

Clive walked across to the window and stared out.

A couple of miles away was the opposite slope of the valley with, almost directly facing Brome House, the house where *they* lived. Mr. Marcus bloody Dymond and his wife. Built sometime during the 1930s, it was pleasant, largish, mock-Tudor style with a garden which had been something of a showpiece until Enid had at last been forced to succumb to her illness and take to a wheelchair. The garden had been her sole interest in life, and she still managed, with the aid of special long-handled tools, to do a very small amount from her chair, but this was limited, owing to the sloping site of the garden, and as far as Clive could gather, the whole thing was becoming a burden. That husband of hers apparently had neither the knowledge nor an enthusiasm equal to hers to cope with it.

So she had nothing to do all day except sit at her window staring through those damned binoculars. Bird watching, she called it, which was another way of saying spying. Spying on the occupants of Brome House and setting her sights on Oddings Cottage, nestling beneath the shelter of the big house. For a moment remorse touched Clive, then a puzzled fury drove it away. How could Dymond have found out? How could he *possibly* have found out?

There was, of course, the boy—though he wouldn't have thought . . . But it must be so; it had to be.

It was Dymond who had sent the letter, of that he was sure, just as he was certain Dymond had sent the others—*and* been the instigator of the telephone calls. Savage thoughts churned in Clive's breast. To hell with him! No way was he going to be intimidated by a jumped-up schoolmaster, or anyone else! Survival of the fittest was what it was all about.

Scrunching up the letter in his fist, the tell-tale vein beginning to jump again at his temple, Clive reached deliberately for the telephone and dialled the number of the Lavenstock Police. Then, before it was answered, he changed his mind and put the receiver back.

Damn Dymond! Damn, damn, damn him.

# CHAPTER 3

After lunch had been cleared away and MacAllister had left, Caroline thrust a letter into her pocket for posting to Pippa, her nine-year-old daughter, who was in Brittany, convalescing after chicken pox, staying with family friends.

She went down the drive, a slim figure in her cream linen suit, walking alongside the front lawn Janice had mown into immaculate stripes. A pile of manuscripts waited her attention, but she needed a breath of air after her busy morning, and moreover to be alone to be able to think over what was to be done. There had been no chance this morning, and last night, after the party, she had been so exhausted she had sunk immediately into oblivion, almost as soon as her head touched the pillow. An oblivion perhaps self-induced, so that she could postpone facing up to the dizzying realisation of what had been admitted, albeit unspokenly, between herself and Matt.

But whether she wanted to think about it or not, it had been there, with her all morning, worrying her, yet making her alive to a new awareness of herself, as if all her life she'd been asleep and untouched until now. Moments of near-panic intervened. Perhaps he didn't after all feel the same way; maybe she'd been imagining . . . But the doubts didn't last long. She knew with certainty that he did. The recognition had been total and mutual.

She shouldn't be allowing herself to think this way—it wasn't playing the game. A phrase of Clive's came to her. "It's only a game, you know," he was wont to say, having done something that had gone too far. Which was all very well, if everyone knew the rules, and stuck to them. Like playing hostess for Clive as part of the game of keeping up appearances, of pretending there was nothing wrong with a marriage that was a blank, a facade, an as yet unvocalised failure.

Why, she asked herself despairingly, had she ever married Clive?

Her mother had died when Caroline was a very young child, leaving her to the tender mercies of her father, a cold and domineering man, under whose influence her own identity as she grew up had struggled to survive. He had taken an instant dislike to Clive as soon as she brought him home—was this why she had uncharacteristically rushed headlong into the marriage? Because she had known that if she didn't make this stand, she herself might sink without trace under the weight of her father's overweening personality? A bid for independence? Or because *Clive* wanted to marry *her*—and Clive always got what he wanted?

Certainly he had warmed her with the energy and fire of his ambition; his vitality had excited her—but love? It was hard to tell, now. When the fire had died down, the gulf between them had gradually widened, and for years they had had nothing in common, except Pippa, the child they both loved so deeply.

Her mind veered away from that old, painful problem, only to be faced with another, newer one.

Lunch, after all, had passed off successfully and pleasantly, which should have pleased Clive, but she wasn't so sure that it had. During the meal, through his favourite pork tenderloin cooked with apples, cream and calvados, to the dark, fragrant coffee and cognac, she had sensed an unusual preoccupation in him. He hadn't been turning the whole battery of his charm—which was considerable when he wanted it to be —on MacAllister, even though he had told her beforehand how important this meeting was to be.

With a sense of foreboding, she had guessed the reasons for its importance. It was all to do with this brash scheme of Clive's to turn Brome House—her home!—into offices. No!

She clenched her fists in the pockets of her skirt. It was out of the question, so wholly unacceptable that it couldn't be thought about. How could Clive even contemplate such a thing? But that was symptomatic of their relationship, that he didn't know how he was hurting her. He should have known, and cared—but it had been a long time since Clive had known what she was thinking, if he ever had. Well, this was something he wasn't going to get his hands on. She was rather shocked at her own way of expressing that—she had, after all, quite willingly surrendered everything else. That she now regretted doing so was another matter—but so was Brome.

Halfway down the drive she turned along a narrow gravel path between clipped yew hedges and into the small, circular walled garden with a cool green pool in the centre, which was her special retreat. The wide stone parapet of the pool, on which she sat, was warm in the sun, roses and clematis clothed the brickwork, a golden carp occasionally flashed from under a lily pad, and through the opening in the wall she could see the house stretched before her in the sunlight.

Maybe it hadn't all that much architectural merit—too many generations of Baddesbys had added or subtracted a wing here, a storey there, changed a window or two according to their own personal idiosyncracies and the fashion of the time—nevertheless it had somehow settled into an unusually charming and attractive whole. Visitors were apt to enthuse about it, and with its mellow red brick and its sweeping pantiled roofs enclosed in the shelter of dark yews, it was photogenic enough to have warranted a recent colour feature in the county magazine. Caroline loved it uncritically; it was her home and she would be quite ruthless in defending it to her last breath.

The sun in the warm enclosed space brought out the incense smell of the thyme, crushed underfoot. It reminded her of being in church, and gradually the same sort of peace stole over her. She didn't have to make a decision about Matt, not yet. He was going away today and she had a whole week to come to terms with herself, so that when they next met, she would surely know how to act.

As she came out of the main gates and set off towards the village post office, she almost bumped into a man who was just emerging from the narrow lane which ran alongside the house.

"Marcus, well, what a surprise!"

As a child, Caroline had often been afraid of this dark, sardonic man with the caustic tongue, and even now she was never quite at ease in his company. Marcus Dymond had been a regular visitor to the house many years ago, in the days when he and her father had played chess together twice a week, a lean, aloof and austere figure. Recently, however, she had scarcely seen him at all. When she visited his invalid wife, he was invariably, and purposely, she fancied, otherwise occupied. Why he didn't want to see her was all too understandable, but what, she wondered, was he doing here now? Coming from the lane that led to Oddings Cottage?

He didn't look particularly pleased to see her, but neither did he seem discomfited. Indeed, he was uncharacteristically forthcoming.

"In the interests of what my doctor is pleased to call fighting the flab, I walk a good deal since my retirement," he remarked with a faintly mocking smile, forestalling any question. "I came down the valley and found myself faced with either a long walk round or, after a somewhat undignified scramble over a fence, the necessity of trespass. I'm afraid I chose the latter."

His spare frame held not an ounce of flab, and he knew as well as she did about the fence. As for trespassing . . . accusing Marcus Dymond of it would be somewhat like forbidding the Pope the freedom of the Vatican.

"I thought of taking a look in at your garden while I was up here and reporting back to Enid," he added. "She still takes an interest, you know."

"You're very welcome. I'll come round with you."

He waved the suggestion away. "No, no, don't bother. A peep through the gates will suffice."

"Why don't you bring Enid up in the car one day? I'm sure she'd love to see the garden again," Caroline said impulsively. "Bring her before the maples are past their best."

"In the highly unlikely event of my ever not being persona non grata at Brome, my dear Caroline, I would willingly do so. As it is . . ."

He left the sentence unfinished, but Caroline could supply the rest.

The last time he had come to the house, he had told Clive exactly what he had thought of him, using such biting sarcasm that even Clive had flinched. She knew that Clive believed Marcus was the one who had been harassing him, and she thought he might have every reason to be afraid of what this man might do, but not in that way. He was capable of malice, certainly, but making anonymous telephone calls— no. His weapons would be more direct—or more subtle.

She looked at him with a troubled face. "I—I'm so terribly sorry."

"You always did have a tender conscience if I mistake not, but I imagine Brome will continue to get on well enough without me, if that's what you meant," Marcus answered dryly.

"I was thinking more of Oddings Cottage. I know you'd set your mind on buying it."

"Not," he replied, lifting a sardonic eyebrow, "at nearly double the price it's worth."

There was very little Caroline felt she could say to mitigate what, after all, had been one of the most indefensible things Clive had ever done. He had *known* the Dymonds were hoping to buy the old cottage when it came on the market. It was really two small one-storey cottages which had been knocked together at some time, and all the rooms being on one level, it would have been ideal for Enid, incapacitated as she now was. Clive, however, had offered way above the asking price, which not unnaturally was promptly accepted, and now Enid must look at it from her window, disappointed, while Clive . . .

Dymond, who had been intently watching her expressive, revealing face, remarked ironically, "One of our more enlightened architects, we must expect to see great things arising from this determination to have the property. Anything less would be quite disgraceful—would it not?"

Before his retirement, Marcus had taught maths at what had once been the old endowed grammar school in Lavenstock and was now, to his deep disapprobation, a comprehensive school. Caroline at this moment saw why his pupils had been reputed to go in such terror of him: she was afraid he was looking right into her mind and reading there just what Clive intended—not to renovate the cottage at all, but to knock it down and rebuild his new modern-style house there, where he hoped to take Pippa and herself to live, so that he could carry out his plans for the big house. The cottage wasn't worth restoring, or so he said; at its best it could only ever have been an Elizabethan slum. Some interfering busybody had got a preservation order put on it, but there were ways and means, he asserted with a laugh, of circumventing that, if you knew what you were about.

"And what if you can't?"

"I don't budget for failure," he'd answered forcibly. "I budget for success, and what's more, I make bloody sure I've got my sums right, so there's no possibility of anything else."

Hurriedly now, she asked Marcus, "How is Enid?"

"A little better, I fancy." He added abruptly, "No, that's not true. She'll never be better; we all know that, don't we? But some days are less worse than others." He paused. "I'll tell her I've seen you, and that you've asked after her. Au revoir, Caroline."

One might have thought Marcus Dymond a man incapable of affection; in reality, Caroline knew his devotion to his wife was utter and complete. This had been especially evident since her illness, something that gave a more sympathetic insight into his difficult character.

"Give her my love, will you? And tell her I'll be down to see her early next week."

Dymond raised his deerstalker and left her.

The silvery chimes of the bracket clock in the dining room were sounding a quarter to four just as Caroline eventually stepped back into the dim coolness of the house. She would have to stir herself if there was any work to be done that afternoon—but first, some tea. She found the kitchen empty and was just about to pick up the kettle when Sylvia Johnson came in, moving in that noiseless way she had, startling Caroline. She carried a tray with used cups and teapot and, when she saw Caroline, exclaimed, "Oh, Mrs. Lethbridge, what a pity, you've just missed tea! But I can soon make some more."

Slightly irritated by the implication that she wasn't prepared to make her own, Caroline felt all the same, glancing at the righteous expression on the girl's face, that she'd better not offer. Sylvia peered into the kettle, saw there was enough water left in it and plugged it in, then reached another blue and white china cup and saucer from the dark oak dresser ranged along one wall. Caroline was surprised to see her hand trembling, enough to make the cup rattle on the saucer.

"Are you all right, Sylvia?"

"Oh yes, quite all right, thank you, Mrs. Lethbridge." In a tone that quite clearly indicated she was not. She began to fuss with preparing the fresh pot of tea.

Oh dear. Sylvia was not a young woman with whom Caroline felt instant rapport—indeed, she found her tiresomely uncommunicative—and though she had tried on the few occasions they'd been alone to find some common ground, she'd so far failed. But clearly now she couldn't, however much she might wish, leave her to her troubles.

"Come on, something's bothering you—what is it, has Mr. Lethbridge been getting at you? He can be a bit sharp sometimes, but he thinks very highly of you, you know—"

"Oh goodness, no, it's not Mr. Lethbridge!" Sylvia answered with such fervour that Caroline looked sharply at her.

Heavens, she couldn't be getting some sort of crush on Clive, could she? She wasn't all that young—old enough to have passed that stage, certainly, Caroline would have thought. "He's never like that with me . . . not unless I've done something really stupid."

"And from what I gather, you don't usually do that, do you?" Caroline smiled, causing a small gleam of self-satisfaction to flash across the other's face. "So what's the trouble?" she repeated, watching Sylvia pour boiling water on to the leaves in the teapot. "Anything I can do to help?"

"It's—it's only—well, the thing is, I can't make my mind up." Sylvia adjusted her slipping spectacles with an ungainly gesture, sliding her forefinger along her nose. Caroline perched on the edge of the table, prepared to listen. "You see, I've had the chance to go to America."

"Well, lucky you!"

"Oh, I don't know about that. But it *was* only temporary, my coming here to work for Mr. Lethbridge, as you know—"

"While Amanda has her baby."

"Yes, but I was beginning to hope—think it might be more permanent, that Amanda might change her mind about coming back after the baby comes." Sylvia fiddled with a spoon, trying to hide her embarrassment.

"That's always a possibility, of course, but if you've had another chance, I should take it. Amanda's very career-minded."

"I know, and my aunt who lives in Boston has got me the promise of this marvellous job there, knowing I only had a temporary position here—and she's sent me my plane ticket and everything." Her plain, sallow face was doleful, her eyes owlish behind the thick spectacles.

"Maybe I'm being obtuse—but what's the problem?"

"I—it's just that I—I don't like leaving Mr. Lethbridge in the lurch."

"Goodness, he'll find someone else easily enough," Caroline said gently. "Jobs like this aren't easy to find; there'll be a queue."

"Ye-es."

"So why the hesitation?"

"I'd rather not say," Sylvia answered primly in a voice little more than a whisper, casting her eyes modestly down.

Caroline looked at the bent head and the lank, mousy hair
dragged back into an unbecoming sort of pony-tail. She'd
been right in her earlier supposition; Sylvia did have a thing
about Clive. Well, it shouldn't be all that surprising. Clive had
considerable physical voltage and could be infinitely charming when it suited him, when anything pleased him, and Sylvia had undoubtedly done that, with her ability to smooth his
path efficiently. Caroline felt very sorry for her; unrequited
love was extremely painful at any age, while it lasted. She
didn't feel it could be serious, but one never knew, and Sylvia
struck her as being deep. Surely she didn't really mean it,
about not going to America?

"Well, I know if I were you, I wouldn't refuse. Opportunities like this don't happen every day, do they? And you say
your aunt's sent you your ticket? When is it for?"

"Next Friday, twelve-fifty from Heathrow," was the
prompt reply, indicating that perhaps the idea hadn't been
dismissed out of hand after all.

"So soon! Friday, that's the fifteenth, isn't it? You're in luck,
as it happens. I have an engagement for lunch not too far
away from the airport. Would you like me to drive you
there?"

For a moment Sylvia looked nonplussed, as if such kindness
didn't often come her way, or perhaps at having her mind
made up for her, but she quickly recovered herself and all of a
sudden said, yes, it would all be for the best, wouldn't it, and
yes, she would appreciate a lift.

Clive wasn't going to be pleased. It would mean finding
another replacement, and not just any old temp either, until
such time as Amanda came back. Caroline decided she would
have to do something herself about this. It might make up for
encouraging Sylvia to leave at such short notice. Though on
reflection she had a strange sort of feeling, that the boot was

on the other foot, that it was she who had been manoeuvred, especially when she remembered that she had asked Sylvia some time ago to make a note in Clive's diary about her lunch appointment in Maidenhead.

# CHAPTER 4

Deep in the intricacies firstly of Baillie-Scott domestic architecture way up on the west coast of Scotland, then Mackintosh's School of Art in Glasgow, Matt had had reason to appreciate the breathing space the last ten days had given him, and the work which necessarily had to occupy the forefront of his mind.

Hitherto, his work as a newspaper and television journalist had taken him to remote and troubled places of the world, where danger and risk were parts of the business he took for granted. He thought he'd learned to put a glass wall between his emotions and that which had to be met and faced in earning his bread and butter. Last year, however, spent in the unspeakable horrors of famine refugee camps in the third world, had put paid to that theory. But only because that damnable recurring dysentery had laid him low, he told himself, debilitating him mentally and physically, leaving him with nothing to fight an almost suicidal despair and anger at the blindness and stupidity of human beings, and bringing him as near a nervous breakdown as ever a man of his sort and condition could come. It had been not only sensible, but necessary, to accept medical advice and opt out for a while, go home and let his mind and body heal.

He had in the early days of his career worked for the architectural press—a long time since now, but a good newspaperman should be able to cover anything, he'd been told when he was a cub reporter still wet behind the ears. So he'd accepted the offer to work in collaboration with Clive on this book, which was concerned with the influence of British architects during the last hundred years on modern European architectural development, the final achievement chosen to illustrate the theme being this greatly acclaimed design of Clive's.

Working with Clive hadn't been easy. Matt was also pretty damn sure Clive was hell to live with, and that was why Caroline was near to breaking point.

Or was she? He had immediately sensed the strains of her marriage when they first met, but he couldn't be sure of her yet, of her strengths and weaknesses—and he would never make the mistake of underrating her capacity for loyalty, or the depth of her love for her daughter. And maybe being on the edge of tension was naturally part of her, a necessary part of her marriage, too—and if it wasn't, what reason had he to think that he, Matt, had anything to do with it?

He'd never experienced anything like this before: up to now, his sex life had been taken care of by transient affairs, unmemorable for anything more than a passing attraction and perhaps a mild affection. He'd believed anything else unnecessary to him and his chosen way of life. Then, this shattering realisation that with Caroline, his needs took on another dimension entirely: a tenderness, a need for her, permanently and totally committed, as he himself already was.

He could be mistaken about her in every way, though on the strength of an answering look, that night of the party, across a crowded room, cornier than corny, he was prepared to believe not. But he sensed there were frontiers she wasn't yet ready to cross, and he had no intention of forcing the pace, of ruining the relationship before it began. The first move might have to come from him, but the final choice must ultimately be hers.

Accordingly, he made himself stay away from Brome for another couple of days after he got back, working in the privacy of his hotel room on the material he had collected. He'd asked for accommodation where the noise of his typewriter and tape-recorder wouldn't be likely to disturb the other guests, and had been given a room in the annexe, which turned out to be pleasanter than in the main building, less overheated and with easier access to the car park and the extensive grounds, where he could stretch his long legs occasionally.

By late afternoon he'd almost finished the final draft of his last night's notes when the telephone rang. It was Caroline.

The full-blooded screams ringing out down the corridor would have done credit to a prima donna, a role for which Mrs. Peach undoubtedly had the physique to qualify, and sometimes the temperament, too. This time she wasn't acting. Her face under her careful make-up drained of colour; then, with no more breath for screaming, she made for the kitchen.

"In the study," was all she could get out at first. "I went in for his tea tray and there he was—oh my God!"

Janice Wharton switched off the chicken soup whizzing round in the food processor, whose noise had prevented her from hearing the screams, and looked up as Mrs. Peach rushed in, a sense of dread clutching her. Her hands reached out to grab the table for support as the meaning sank in. She stood rigid, her blue-overalled figure silhouetted against the cheerful red Aga.

"Is he—he isn't—?" she began, in a dry, hurting whisper.

"I think," announced Mrs. Peach, "I'm going to faint—or be sick."

Torn between necessities, Janice took a few jerky, uncoordinated steps, hesitating between Mrs. Peach and the door.

"Don't!" The older woman recovered with speed as Janice's hand finally reached for the knob. "Don't you go into that there study, Janice, for God's sake. There isn't nothing you can do, anyway."

Caroline was aware of something out of the ordinary as soon as she had parked her car in the garage, formerly one of the old stables. For one thing, Mrs. Peach's orange Volkswagen beetle was still there, K registration and looking as if it had emerged from the showroom yesterday. One careful lady owner, in this case no contradiction in terms, as Clive had once remarked with a rare spark of humour.

The sense persisted as she opened the kitchen door, where an unnatural silence reigned, rather than the activity usual at this hour, when the evening meal was normally well under way. Also very oddly, Mrs. Peach was sitting at the old-fashioned scrubbed-top table, leaning back ostentatiously with her eyes closed, the teapot and the brandy bottle in front of her. Janice was crouched against the Aga, as if, despite the warmth of the evening, she needed all the heat she could extract from its slow-ticking oven.

"Still here, Mrs. Peach? Shouldn't you be at home by now?"

The older woman sprang to her feet. "Oh, Caroline!"

Mrs. Peach had known Caroline since she was a little girl, and she was the last person in the world to be deliberately cruel, but now that she was recovering somewhat from the initial shock, her natural sense of drama was returning fast. She clutched her hands in front of her imposing bosom. "There's been a terrible accident!"

Caroline stopped abruptly, halfway across the kitchen. She forced herself to say it. "It's Pippa. It's Pippa, isn't it?"

"No, no, m'duck, thank God it's not her!"

"I think you'd better sit down." Janice threw a look at Mrs. Peach, pulled herself together, and since "accident" wasn't to her an acceptable euphemism for murder, told Caroline straightly what had happened.

Then, as Caroline stood transfixed, they heard the sound of the first of the cars arriving.

"Who found him?"

By the time the investigating officer arrived, Detective Chief Inspector Gil Mayo from Divisional Headquarters in Lavenstock, ten minutes behind his sergeant, the sombre routine machinery of violent death was already rolling smoothly into action. The room was thick with photographers, the scenes-of-crime team, and the grey dust of fingerprint powder. The police surgeon arrived, pronounced life extinct, and now that the photographer had finished with his stills and his video camera, was ready to examine the body further.

"Mrs. Peach," answered Sergeant Kite, who'd already been gleaning information from P.C. Trenchard, the local man. "Lady from the village who helps to clean two or three times a week."

"Hm." Mayo stood in the centre of the room, being careful not to move about too much, so as not to disturb the evidence, looking impassive, even bored. A tall, solidly built Yorkshireman, just the wrong side of forty, with thick, strong hair, disciplined from its inclination to curl by a short haircut, deep-set eyes that could disconcert by their concentrated observation, he was by nature not inclined to speak overmuch. Now he stood silently, taking it all in, absorbing all-important first impressions of his surroundings, getting a gut feeling about the case. His trained eye ranged round the room, noting each feature and filing it for further use.

The room was a shambles, but that couldn't disguise dark oak panelling, good, solid furniture with the sort of patina that only came from years of dedicated polishing, several very good modern paintings and some old oriental rugs, their blues and reds softened by time. One wall was devoted to framed photographs of what was presumably the work of the dead man—municipal buildings, an art gallery, dozens of houses, a factory or two. Some had been knocked askew in the violent attack on the room, but none had been broken. His glance passed on, coming back to the body.

Mayo was necessarily familiar with death in its more horrific manifestations, but appearances to the contrary, he hadn't yet come to regard it with indifference, become casehardened as some of his colleagues were—or allegedly so. Well, everybody had to learn to cope in their own way, and his was total detachment, as far as this was possible. Shut your mind off from everything but the hard facts, the input that fed the computer called the brain, and don't cloud the issue by being squeamish, or emotional. Difficult. Nearly im-

possible, but you'd damn well better do it. It was there, a
crime to be solved. Violent death, the ultimate silencer, the
irrevocable end, somebody's answer to jealousy, greed, revenge, fear. Always shocking, and evil hanging wherever it
had occurred, like a miasma. In this room now, like the smell
of blood, and of death itself.

Clive Lethbridge was still in the position he had been
found, slumped forward over his desk, arms outspread, his
head slightly to one side, the back of it brutally smashed in.
Dark, sticky blood, greyish brain tissue and fragments of
white bone were matted in with the thick, wiry hair.

There was blood all over. It had spattered the walls and the
curtains and the windows and the back and sleeves of the
cream silk shirt the victim was wearing, and run down behind his left ear to soak his collar, and spread out on to the
papers beneath his head and body. God, a right old mess.

"Probably stunned with one blow from behind, then killed
by further blows," the doctor pronounced, straightening up.
"All that blood. Indicates the heart went on pumping for
some time after the first blow. Which was made with something heavy, with a sharp edge—and used with considerable
force, I might say."

"With something like that, for instance."

Ison followed Mayo's pointing finger to where an extremely handsome and heavy cut-glass inkwell lay rolled on
its side on the carpet, its brilliant refractions winking in the
evening sun which streamed through the open french window. Surmounted by a domed, cut and faceted lid mounted in
silver and hinged to the base, it was a half-sphere, about the
size and shape of half a coconut, with a small hollow designed
for ink, when being put to its original use. A deeply cut pattern of vertical incisions segmented it, continuing underneath the base to repeat and catch prismatic reflections from
each other. The glittering ruby highlights, so pretty in the
sun, came from the dried blood on the serrations at the edge
of the base, which, Mayo had no doubt, would match exactly
the jagged edges of the wounds in the smashed skull.

"Probably." Ison in fact had no doubts either, but caution was second nature to him. "The P.M. will make certain."

"How long's he been dead?"

"Not all that long. According to the body temperature, and the temperature in here, which is warm, about an hour, I'd say."

"Four twenty-five?"

"Give or take."

Ison rolled down his sleeves and side-stepped the scenes-of-crime officer, D.C. Dexter, who knelt on the floor, hands encased in thinly stretched, transparent protective gloves. At that moment he was lifting the inkwell with extreme care, preparatory to packing it in a sterile container. Besides the blood adhering to it, there would almost certainly be minute traces of skin and hair and brain tissue . . . though probably, unless the murderer had been particularly careless, no fingerprints. Villains nowadays saw too many TV cop shows.

"Strewth, heavier than it looks, this, must weigh all of four or five pounds, I reckon," Dexter grunted.

"Lead crystal, by the look of it. Victorian, at a guess, wouldn't you say, Kite?"

"I wouldn't know." The tall, lanky sergeant eyed the ornate piece of craftsmanship disparagingly. "Not the sort of thing I go for myself . . . even supposing I could afford it." The expression on his slightly ingenuous, normally cheerful face endorsed his opinion of the richly comfortable circumstances that the deceased had apparently enjoyed. "Easy enough to handle, though, I should think. Get a good grip on the silver mounting, with the lid in your palm, and bingo!"

"A man's hand, yes. Or both of a woman's."

"Hardly a woman's crime, though, is it?" the doctor commented, snapping his case shut. "Nasty, brutal."

Mayo said, "You'd be surprised, some of the women I've known."

Ison, packing his instruments, conceded the point with a wry smile. "As you say."

But male or female, one-handed or two-handed, the murderer had operated from behind. The desk over which Leth-bridge slumped was a very large one, almost square, the kind known as a partners' desk, with drawers back and front, and was set towards the centre of the room, and at an oblique angle to the window. When he was attacked, he had been sitting facing the room, his back to the garden. The french windows were wide open, and fastened back.

"So he either knew his murderer, and therefore was unsus-pecting when he moved behind him for some reason—or somebody crept up from outside and did for him," said Kite.

Ison nodded. "Either way, the first blow would have knocked him out sufficient to quieten him, if that was all that was wanted, even if it didn't actually kill him. The rest was either making sure or just being vindictive."

"Whichever, he was disturbed in the middle of what he was doing, wasn't he?" Kite leaned gingerly forward, peering over the dead man's shoulder. A pencil was still gripped be-tween the fingers of his right hand, and a long, deep line from where the large, confident handwriting stopped had scored the only visible page, most of which, however, was obscured by the rusty stain of dried blood.

"As soon as you can," Mayo remarked to Dexter, with a nod at the mess on the desk, "get me the lab report on that. I'd like to know what he was working on."

Things moved with speed and efficiency when Mayo was around, but he was inclined to expect results the day before yesterday. "Do my best, sir, but you know how it is. We're up to our eyes as usual." He met Mayo's grey stare. "Yes, right. Right, sir."

"We all have our problems," said Ison, and left.

Mayo walked to the window, thinking about the layout of the house. The study was a double-aspected room, set on the corner of the house, with long views of the gardens and the gravelled main drive, which divided outside the study to sweep round, encircling the entire house. Flanking the drive were rose beds and herbaceous borders. There was a yew hedge at some distance, and a shrubbery alongside the road.

At the back were extensive lawns, beyond which lay an orchard.

"Any idea where that leads?" he asked Kite, pointing to a path crossing the lawn, apparently opening on to a lane which separated the property from the adjoining one.

"According to Trenchard, eventually up on to the Lavenstock Road. A bit of a scramble, and private property anyway, though apparently that doesn't stop anybody. It's a favourite picnic spot down by the stream."

"Did he say who owns the place next door?"

"Chap called Comstock—runs a stud farm. He uses the lane for access, but it belongs to Brome House. They seem to use it mostly for delivery of heating oil and stuff for the garden."

A wide area just outside the french window had already been cordoned off. Some of the gravel from the drive was on the carpet just inside the window, not necessarily brought in by the murderer since there was also a small gritty patch of it under the pedestal of the desk, near the dead man's feet in their highly polished tan slip-on shoes.

"Terrible stuff, gravel, for treading indoors," Kite said feelingly, watching Dexter, who was still crawling about on the floor, scoop the two separate lots into plastic bags, seal and label them. His wife had briskly refused to have it laid on the drive of their new house, especially with the kids running in and out and herself busy with her new career. She'd opted for mock-stone slabs instead. You wouldn't have thought it could do much harm to the rugs in here, though. Tatty old specimens, Sheila wouldn't give them house room. Spoiled the look of the good fitted carpet they were spread on.

"Not quiet, either," added Mayo absently, staring down at the Georgian console table which stood between the window and the bookcase, its bare top greyish now with fingerprint powder. Was that where the inkwell had stood, conveniently to hand for any intruder? It was the only flat surface of its kind in the room that had not apparently been holding some bibelot or objet d'art, though it was difficult to tell in the chaos of the room.

"Anything strike you as odd about this lot, Martin?"

Kite looked at the cushions thrown on the floor, the pictures knocked off the straight, books swept to the floor. "Not very convincing, is it?" he said, after a moment's thought.

"Right. As if somebody in too big a hurry to take much trouble wanted to suggest robbery as a motive for the killing. Or," he added thoughtfully, "as a cover-up for destroying this thing here—the only thing that *has* actually suffered any damage, you'll notice."

"What is it?"

Mayo was peering down at the baize-covered table on which remained all that was left of the Svensen Centre model, a heap of Perspex and balsa, recognisable for what it had once been only by the metal label which had been fixed to the base. "Model of some sort. Must have been that hospital or whatever he won that prize with. Wasn't there a picture in last week's *Advertiser?*"

"And a big write-up. I remember. Clever bloke."

"Well paid for it, any road," remarked Mayo, beginning to prowl around the room, carefully avoiding touching anything, "if this house and what's in it's anything to go by."

"Well, likely this is all family stuff. Wife's family," Kite added, having forgotten for the moment that Mayo, being newish to the division, might not know this. "The Baddesbys, been grinding the faces of the poor around here since Adam was a lad, and not short of a bob or two, neither."

Mayo made no answer to this beyond a swift, sharp glance at Kite. He twisted his head sideways to look closer at a modern painting hanging wildly askew. "This wasn't handed down, though." If it was indeed an original Hockney, it hadn't been given away with cornflake tops, either.

Kite did his best not to avert his eyes from it. "Well, it takes all sorts," he said at last, not being able to think of anything else to say and uncertain as to whether his gaffer might actually be admiring the painting.

Kite hadn't quite got the measure of Mayo yet, what really made him tick; they'd only worked together on a few cases so

far. Despite that blunt Yorkshire facade, he seemed easy
enough, yet Kite had the feeling it wouldn't do to push your
luck with him. Wasn't married, though he had been once;
whether widowed or divorced was still a matter of specula-
tion in the division. He had a daughter, but he didn't invite
questions about his personal life. Truth to tell, he seemed to
be something of a loner, a mite austere. He didn't smoke, play
games or even follow them, not even cricket, which for a
Yorkshireman must be tantamount to treason. It was
rumoured that he liked music, the heavy stuff, symphonies
and that. He read a lot.

But Kite wasn't going to hold that against him. He was
disposed to like Mayo. He was a damned good policeman,
with a steady record of success behind him, and a seemingly
predictable future ahead in the way of promotion prospects.
He was fair, and didn't hog the limelight. Kite wouldn't have
resented this last anyway. Having sweated to reach sergeant
early, his own desire for promotion had received an unexpected check. Give it time, he told himself; it takes time to
adjust to the idea and circumstances of two ambitious parents
in one happy family.

Happy, he repeated. That's right. They'd work it out, sure
they would.

A scrunch of gravel under tyres announced the arrival of
the mortuary van. They watched, soberly, as Clive Lethbridge's body, plastic-sheeted, was carried out.

"Right, then," Mayo said abruptly, "let's get moving. Can't
afford to waste time." He moved across to the small room
adjoining the study and peered in. Little more than a cubby-
hole with a desk occupying one wall and an electronic typewriter standing on it, plus a filing cabinet, a plan chest and a
photocopier. The room at present was crammed to capacity
with a large fingerprint man and the photographer. "We'll
make a start on that lot when the lads have finished, see what
turns up. Farrar can give me a hand. The rest of the house I'll
leave you to organise."

Kite looked gloomy. "Not exactly a semi, is it?" He thought

of attics and cellars, the kitchen, a vast room so old-fashioned it was trendy again, and a bathroom which still had its original mahogany seat. God knew how many bedrooms. Folks with so much room they never threw anything away.

"Take you a bit longer, that's all. I'll see you're not short-handed. You can have Deeley."

Kite rolled up his eyes.

Despite a regrettable tendency to flippancy, Mayo knew Kite was conscientious and thorough, often acute, and that he could rely on him. He thought that given time, they'd make a good team. "Cheer up, son. There's none of us here for a good night's kip. Meanwhile, let's get the day's pattern established —who came and went, where he'd been, who he'd been seeing and so on."

Kite pulled out his notebook. "According to Mrs. Wharton, he didn't go out, had no visitors. He was working alone here all day, had lunch alone, and tea."

"That simplifies things—who's Mrs. Wharton?"

"Yet another of the helpers in the house . . . Gawd, how the other half lives!"

Hands in pockets, Mayo surveyed his sergeant. "Pack it in, lad."

Kite's round, candid face assumed innocence.

"Now you've got it out of your system, can we contrive to manage without the snide socialism, and get on with the business?"

"Yes, sir; sorry, sir." Kite, whose leftist sympathies had long been little more a habit, had merely been firing token shots, more as a gesture of independence than anything else. He looked sheepish and consulted his notes. "Tea was brought in about half-three by Mrs. Peach, give or take a few minutes. At five to five, when she came in to collect the tray before going home, he was dead. Which more or less squares with what Doc Ison tells us."

"An hour and a half, during which he wasn't entirely alone. Somebody must have heard or seen something. What about his wife?"

"She's been out all day."

"Oh, where?"

"I don't know yet. Shall we have her in and ask her?"

Mayo thought about it. "Yes."

Kite poked his head round the door and spoke to the detective constable, Deeley, on duty in the corridor outside. Mayo heard a muffled altercation, and then Kite was back in the room, with Deeley in front of him and the door closed behind him. "It seems," he announced, "that Mrs. Lethbridge has gone out again."

# CHAPTER 5

"Gone out? *Out?*" Although Mayo addressed Deeley quietly enough, Kite felt the draught from where he stood. "I thought you said she came home just before we arrived?"

"Yes, sir, she did, but she went out again. By the back door, sir," answered Deeley, a beefy young man who occasionally, like now, wondered if he was in the right job, detecting criminals. Maybe he should have stayed on the beat, rather than going through all that grief to get into C.I.D. He'd give a week's pay to be back there right now. "I understand she's gone to see a Mr. Waring, sir. He only lives in the next village."

A look passed between Mayo and Kite. Mayo turned back to Deeley, the cross he'd had to bear since coming to Lavenstock. "Then it shouldn't take you long to get over there and fetch her back, should it?" he asked, more mildly. Deeley was heavy weather, with no imagination whatsoever, but there was room for the plodders as well as the high-flyers. So they said. "What's keeping you?"

"Nothing, sir, only there's Mrs. Peach, the cleaning lady. She's waiting to be off home. Says her husband'll be shouting for his tea."

Mayo thought for a moment. "All right. I'll see her now." He stood up and followed Kite and Deeley out of the room. "Mrs. Peach?" he said to the woman waiting outside. "Sorry if we've kept you hanging about, but we shouldn't be much longer now. Is there somewhere we can talk for a few minutes?"

"I suppose," Mrs. Peach answered stiffly, unappeased, "we could go into the garden room."

"That would be useful, thank you."

She marched along the thickly carpeted corridor and led the way into a room farther along, filled with evening sunlight and furnished with a haphazard selection of cushioned armchairs slip-covered in faded cretonne, together with a rubbed yellow velvet sofa and one or two bookcases and occasional tables, on one of which stood a huge bowl of old-fashioned cream Provence roses, deeply scented. Photographs in profusion lined the walls, a television set stood in one corner, and two latticed french windows led out on to a paved terrace overlooking another aspect of the main garden. An unpretentious, slightly shabby room, it had a comfortable air of being much used.

Mrs. Peach removed the roses to a corner bookcase, very pointedly, and only then indicated to Mayo that he might now be permitted to use the table.

"Thank you; please sit down." Mayo waved her to an armchair and sat down himself in an elderly one with a sagging seat facing her, which turned out to be surprisingly comfortable. "Now, Mrs. Peach, let's have a few details."

He leaned back, leaving the note-taking to Kite, ready to concentrate on the answers to his questions, trying to pick up the hesitancies and nuances of conversation, as well as the apparent irrelevancies which interviewees were apt to pursue, and which could be so revealing about the person being questioned.

In this case Beryl Peach, a spritely, full-bosomed lady, fifty-three years old, with a strong Midlands accent. Worked here since Mrs. Lethbridge was a little girl, she had, before her mother—Caroline's mother, that was, Mrs. Baddesby—died. Came every morning except Friday, when she came in the afternoon.

"That's my afternoon for the silver, and odd jobs like that. It's not convenient for me to come here of a Friday morning, see," she added independently. "It's when I do my weekend shopping up in Lavenstock and then go on to have my hair done after." She patted her Silver Pearl-rinsed curls.

"Very nice," remarked Mayo, seeing some comment was called for, and feeling the effort was worthwhile when she unbent so far as to look faintly mollified, though she never took her round, somewhat beady eyes from his face for a minute. The stare unnerved him a little.

"So you saw Mr. Lethbridge when you took his tea in to him. What time was that?"

"Just before half past three."

"Did he have anything to eat with it?"

"A couple of my buttered scones, that I always make a batch of on Fridays. I don't usually do the cooking, but Janice hasn't got such a light hand with scones, and he did enjoy one or two with his tea."

"How did he seem when you went in? As usual?"

"He was standing in front of the window, and he didn't turn round, just told me to put the tray down. And the next time I saw him, when I come back for the tray, soon as I opened the door, there he was, dead!" She lifted a handkerchief to her eyes.

"How did you know that?

The handkerchief was lowered abruptly. "Well, he didn't hit hisself on the head, did he, and he looked dead enough to me, dead as mutton!"

"What I mean is, you must have walked right into the room in order to see the condition he was in."

"I did; I thought at first, before I got near to him, he'd just been took bad, but I didn't touch him, if that's what you mean! I told Janice—Mrs. Wharton—you should never touch the body. However, she said we ought to make sure—what if he was still alive? You wouldn't have got me back into that study, not for King Dick. But she would have it. However, I was right, wasn't I?" On a much more subdued note. He saw she was much upset underneath the histrionics.

"Yes, Mrs. Peach, I'm afraid you were. I do realise this has been a very nasty experience for you, but you've been very helpful so far. What time did you fetch the tray back?"

"About five to five, just before I was ready to go home, like I always do."

By which time Lethbridge had probably been dead just over half an hour. "Now—this Mr. Waring, this gentleman Mrs. Lethbridge has rushed off to see . . . Very good friend of the family, is he?"

"Yes, he is, but there's no hanky-panky going on there, so don't you go insinuating there is!" Mrs. Peach retorted with spirit. "Mr. Waring must be sixty if he's a day, I'll have you know."

Mayo reckoned he hardly had a good twenty years left to him, on that basis. He avoided Kite's eye and said mildly, "I was only wondering, why him? Why Mr. Waring in particular? And why Mrs. Lethbridge didn't simply telephone?"

"Oh, the telephone! Not much sympathy from a telephone, is there? Besides, I've told you—he's a close friend. Mr. Lethbridge's partner and ever such a nice gentleman, he is. He only lives over at Addencote, anyway, not more than five minutes in the car."

"I see. Well, let's get back to Mr. Lethbridge. As an employer, what was he like?"

"I've no complaints. He was always all right with me. It was only with them as give him old buck that he got a bit nas —a bit worked up."

Here we go again, thought Mayo, the old speak-no-ill-of-the-dead syndrome that was, however, often more revealing than the truth. "Short-tempered, was he? The sort to make enemies?"

"I wouldn't know about that," Mrs. Peach answered primly.

"Hm. Were you responsible for cleaning the study?"

"Only on Thursday. Janice saw it had a once-over every day, then I always give it a real good do of a Thursday, because he worked at home most Fridays and he was very particular about everything being kept nice and polished."

"As soon as we can, we'll get you to have a look and see if there's anything missing. You'd know, of course?"

"Oh, definitely!"

"I suppose I can rely on Mrs. Wharton for the same thing?"

"You can rely on Janice for anything; good as gold, she is, not like that husband of hers." She bit her lip and stood up hurriedly, aware that the brandy she'd consumed had loosened her tongue. "If that's all, I'd like to get off."

But Mayo, realising he had before him God's gift to policemen, a loquacious witness, was not prepared to let her go just yet. "Another minute or two, if you don't mind." With a heavy, resigned sigh, Mrs. Peach sat down again. "I'm sorry to keep you, but you see, in a case like this," Mayo went on, using unashamed flattery, "it's important to talk to people who are observant and keep their eyes and ears open. Somebody like you, who'd know for instance if Mr. and Mrs. Lethbridge didn't get on well together."

"Oh no, there was nothing like that! What I mean is, they got on as well as most."

"I suppose they had their differences, like most married couples?"

"Not in front of me, they didn't," she answered firmly.

He saw that her loyalty to Caroline Lethbridge was paramount, and decided to press the advantage. "You've known Mrs. Lethbridge since she was a little girl, you say, so it must have pleased you to see her happy."

"Happy?" The exclamation was out before she could stop it. She bit her lip, then said soberly, "I never said she was happy." There was a longer silence, then suddenly, with another sigh, she gave up pretending. "I only wish she was. I don't know what it is, but it seems to me something's been wrong for quite a while now."

"Money troubles?"

"Oh, I wouldn't say that . . . but I don't know, a house like this doesn't run on fresh air, does it? They didn't seem short to me, but that's all according. All I can say is, things weren't as they should be."

Mayo thought that she was almost certainly telling the truth, and that she knew no more than she had told him. He questioned her a little more about the day-to-day routine of the house, then said, "That's about it, Mrs. Peach, for now. As you found the body, we'll need you to make a signed statement, but it'll do later, when we've finished with the room. I take it you'd have no objection?"

Clearly, Mrs. Peach had not. It didn't often come her way to play the leading lady. All in all, it was quite a red-letter day in her life.

"I thought we'd ruled out thieving as a motive." Kite asked when she'd gone.

"We haven't ruled anything out yet, lad."

Mayo stood looking out of the window, which faced directly on to a great cedar of Lebanon, possibly two hundred years old, its wide arms sweeping the lawn beneath the terrace. He hated the disorientated feeling at the beginning of investigations of this sort, before you could see the shape of the case and you were still fumbling around, seeking which direction to go in to find the answer. "We both know murderers who've killed for reasons neither you nor I would recognise as a motive at all—but motive of some sort we've got to look for. Unless we're faced with a psychopath, who just happened along and clobbered him to death for the hell of it . . . which is possible, all right, but I think we'll stick with the other . . . that's what we're looking for. And having seen that lot in there, I think it more than likely somebody must have finished up looking like an assistant in a ritual slaughterhouse."

"So how'd they get away, looking like that? They'd be taking a hell of a risk."

"Maybe it was someone who didn't need to get away. Maybe they were here already." Mayo stepped out of the french window, fastened back with a hook to the wall. "With this open, I doubt if he'd be taken by surprise," he said, crunching his feet on the gravel to make his point.

# CHAPTER 6

Mrs. Peach, her coat on and handbag over her arm like the
Queen Mother, found Caroline, brought back from Addencote, with Harry Waring in the shadowed drawing room.
The sun had gone from this side of the house, where the oak-
panelled walls and the huge, sombre pictures absorbed even
more light. Caroline looked very small, curled in the corner
of the Knole settee, as if she wanted to hide in its high-backed
depths, her face a white blur against the dark blue brocade.

She had felt numb ever since she had been told of Clive's
death, she didn't seem able to take it in yet, she was frozen
inside, white-faced and withdrawn behind a wall of silence.

"They say they'll see you now, seeing as you're here, Mr.
Waring," Mrs. Peach announced, as if she'd personally arranged it, and to Caroline, "What's-his-name, that there inspector, says I can go now, so if it's all the same to you, I
ought to be off."

Harry stubbed out his cigar, reduced the level of whisky in
the heavy Waterford crystal by half an inch, stood up, gave
Caroline's shoulder a rather helpless squeeze, and said to Mrs.
Peach, "Can't you stay with her until I get back?"

"Oh, for heaven's sake, Harry, I'm not a child! Don't you
see, that's just what I *want*, to be alone." Caroline was roused
enough from her lethargy to protest, in a sharp way so uncharacteristic of her they both looked at her in surprise. "I'm
sorry," she said. "You've been so kind, you've all been so
kind . . ."

"It doesn't matter." Harry patted her shoulder again and
went out.

Mrs. Peach said matter-of-factly, "With all them policemen

trampling all over the house with their big feet and drinking us out of tea and coffee, we're likely to run a bit short—shall I bring some more instant when I come tomorrow? No point in giving that lot fresh."

"If you think so," Caroline answered colourlessly, but that didn't satisfy Mrs. Peach.

"What I *do* think is, you should have something to eat. Why don't you try just a drop of that chicken soup Janice made? You won't do no good starving yourself. And what are you doing sitting in the dark?" She reached out and bossily switched on a lamp.

Caroline blinked, defenceless in the sudden radiance. "I might have some later," she answered evasively, though the last thing she wanted was food.

"I know how you feel, m'duck," the older woman said unexpectedly, and hesitated, as if about to offer more sympathy, then evidently thought better of the idea. "However, I should have a try to eat something. It'll do you good."

"I'll try, I promise."

Mrs. Peach was clearly unconvinced, but she gave a nod. "Well, see you do. I'd better love you and leave you now, and go and get Arthur his tea—his supper by now, I suppose it'll be. He'll be hopping mad, he will, but he'd starve to death before he'd lift a finger to get cracking hisself." Yet unexpectedly she felt an affection for Arthur that hadn't been expressed for a long time. After all, even a husband like Arthur was better than none at all.

At last she took her departure, leaving Caroline staring at the smoke from Harry's abandoned cigar spiralling in the lamplight, wrestling with the guilt that was the uppermost emotion in her mind.

"I suppose they want to see me next," she said when Harry came back, making a beeline for the drink he had left. "Oh God."

"They haven't said so—but there's nothing to be nervous

about. That chief inspector chap seems pretty decent—just tell the truth, and you'll be all right."

"The truth, yes," Caroline murmured, her pulses jerking. Harry was contemplating what was left of his cigar as if wondering whether it was worth re-lighting. "Why did you ask to see them, Harry? What have they been asking you? You've been in the office all day, haven't you? You couldn't have had anything to do with it."

"Presumably I could tell them something about those who could have," Harry replied selectively. "They did ask me a lot of questions."

"Such as?"

"Oh, the usual sort of stuff, I suppose, when they're looking for—well, you know, in a case like this—the people he had contact with, both here and in the office—whether Clive had any enemies and such like. They seemed very interested," he added carefully, "in the letters, and the calls."

Caroline stiffened. "The anonymous letters? How did you know about them?"

"Why, Clive. Clive told me. Does that surprise you?"

"Since he told me not to say a word to anyone, and vowed he wouldn't either, yes, it does. He was quite adamant that the only thing to do with poison like that was to ignore it."

"And he was right, of course. All the same, he did mention them to me."

Caroline's nervous fingers twisted the decorative fringe on the high side of the settee. A strand of it came loose.

"Did he tell you who he thought was sending them?"

"As a matter of fact, he did."

"And you told the detective? So that was why you asked to see him!"

"I had to, Caroline. We can't any of us have any secrets now."

Caroline felt the colour rising in her cheeks, but if Harry noticed, he apparently mistook the cause. "I can understand your reluctance to name names, but Marcus Dymond," he said gently, "is already implicated. He was here this morning —and they had a blazing row, he and Clive."

"Marcus? *Here?*"

"Unfortunately for him, yes." Her patent incredulity prompted him to add, "Marcus told me so himself, on the telephone, after he'd been here. He rang me, demanding information, which I naturally refused to give him."

"About what?"

"I could only infer," Harry said cautiously, "that he must have learned about Clive's plans for Oddings Cottage."

Another shock. She hadn't known this, either, that Harry was a party to those particular proposals . . . though of course she ought to have realised, as Clive's partner, it was on the cards he would be. As though he felt her unspoken censure, as if in his own defence, Harry added, "I didn't feel it necessary to tell the police what I believed the row with Clive was about, because I may be totally wrong. I only know Dymond was absolutely livid about something."

"But he didn't murder Clive!"

"How do you know?" he asked, rather quickly.

"I—well, I just do. Marcus would *never* do anything like that; it's not his style." Whatever his faults, one had to be fair to him. "Oh, I know what he's like, and what the situation was between him and Clive, but he's simply not capable of murder."

"We're all capable of it," Harry said heavily. "We all have the seeds of violence in us. All it needs is enough provocation."

She gave him a frightened look. But yes—no one could deny that Clive had annoyed and upset so many people, not only Marcus.

It was always possible, of course, that Marcus had on this occasion found it too much and had acted irrevocably, but could anyone truly believe this? "Harry, do you know exactly what those letters said? Clive never actually showed me one."

Harry paused. "He never showed me, either." He stood up, finally discarding the cigar. "My dear, won't you change your mind and come back home with me? Cynthia will never forgive me if I leave you alone tonight. She'd have been here if she hadn't been staying in town until tomorrow . . . She'll be kicking herself as it is."

Caroline was sure she would. The thought at this moment of Harry's divorced sister, Cynthia, with whom he had shared a house since his wife's death . . . Cynthia, immaculate, organised, her tireless advice and her ceaselessly jangling bracelets, was insupportable.

"Thank you; it's thoughtful of you, Harry, but I'd rather be here—and I shall hardly be alone, shall I, with half the Lavenstock police force on the premises? There is something you can do for me, though, if you want to help . . . If—if you could phone the Pelhams in Brittany . . . and tell them what's happened. There's no need for Pippa—" She swallowed hard. "—there's no need for Pippa to come home just now. And I'd be grateful if they can keep it from her until I can tell her myself . . ."

"Pippa, oh God, yes, I'd forgotten her, poor child!" Harry exclaimed, with more feeling than tact. For a moment, as his eyes rested on Caroline's pinched, withdrawn face, he fell silent, then he said briskly, "Yes, I can at least do that for you, my dear. And if it's really what you want, to be left alone, then I won't press you." She thought she detected a faint relief on his face, and was glad she'd refused. "Good night, and I'll see you in the morning." His kiss on her cheek was awkwardly kind as he parted from her at the door, leaving her blessedly alone.

Alone, yes. But what she really wanted was Matt, strong and comforting, able to cut through the tangled knot of her fears, here beside her when, she thought with a kind of terror, he was the very last person who must be brought into it.

The soft scents and sounds of the evening garden surrounded her as she stepped outside a minute or two after Harry's car had disappeared down the drive. The sky was a pale green, deepening to orange, with a single star. It was very quiet, her own footsteps on the gravel the only sound,

save for the more distant drone of an aircraft and a dog's
sudden, sharp bark, the soft whinny of the horses in the Com-
stocks' paddock.

In contrast, the house itself, usually silent and peaceful at
this hour of a summer evening, or perhaps with music coming softly from one of its rooms, was restless with the movement of police. Lights were on everywhere, in unaccustomed
places, in unused rooms, and suddenly everything familiar
was bewildering; even the garden where she stood was alien
territory, the deepening shadows under the cedar held terror,
and for the first time, the absolute reality of Clive's death hit
her.

Clive was dead. Clive, so overwhelmingly full of life, so
sure of himself. Uncontrollably, she shivered.

An owl swooped silently, like a great grey moth against the
sky. Gravel scrunched, and the detective chief inspector, tall
and broad in the dusk, drew level with her.

Facing him later, across the table in the garden room, it
struck her that she had never encountered a detective before,
other than on the TV screen. This one wouldn't have stood a
chance for a role on the box, being neither outstandingly
handsome nor outstandingly tough, though he was a little bit
of both. He had an air of quiet authority, his questions were
polite but direct; there was nothing soft about him. You
wouldn't be wise to play around with him. Her heart began
to beat a little faster.

The lanky sergeant came in and sat down, taking out his
notebook.

Routinely, she was asked her full name, her age, how long
she had been married. "Ten years," said Caroline, "nearly
eleven."

Mayo studied her, taking her measure while she answered
him, deciding which approach to use in questioning her. A
soft sweep of dark hair, limpid, troubled blue eyes, a formal
and elegant silk dress, the colour of autumn beech leaves, soft
bronze leather shoes. He would have put her at less than

thirty-three, perhaps because initially that vulnerable look was one you normally didn't see much, beyond youth. She had an indefinable air of having been sheltered all her life, accustomed to luxury and soft living, with her expensive clothes and perfume, her pampered skin and shining hair; but her luminous eyes were steady and intelligent, and her responses quick.

"Have you any children?"

"One. Philippa, we call her Pippa; she's nine. Luckily, she's staying with friends." For the first time, Caroline faltered. Mayo watched her eyes turn involuntarily towards one of the photographs on the wall, a snapshot of a small child on a beach, with a large, chunky man crouched beside her, father and daughter laughing into the camera.

This was something he was never easy about, the pressing for advantage when a witness was most defenceless, though he didn't shirk the duty, and at once began to question her closely about her movements during the day, pausing after a while to recap. "So you drove straight from here to Heathrow this morning, deposited Miss—Johnson, that's right, isn't it, yes, Johnson, to catch her flight to Boston, and then on to Maidenhead for lunch. What time did you leave there?"

"Just after two, about five past, I think. We had lunch early because Mr. Conti and his wife had another appointment. That's why I saw him at home, rather than at his London office, as I usually do . . . Besides, I know them as old family friends, as well as in business, you see."

"What business is that?"

"Mr. Conti is a publisher, and I work for him as a reader—that is, I read manuscripts and make recommendations about publishing. Or not, as the case may be." She immediately wished she had not added the explanation; it appeared patronising, as though a mere policeman couldn't be expected to know what a publisher's reader did. The concentrated regard didn't waver, however. He merely remarked that it sounded interesting work.

"I find it so."

"And you left at five past two then, and got home at what time?"

"Twenty past five," Caroline replied, her eyes darkening at the memory of that awful moment when she had walked into the kitchen, every detail of which would be implanted in her mind forever.

Kite cleared his throat and, over her bent head, exchanged glances with his chief. Mayo answered the sergeant's unspoken request to take up the questioning with a barely perceptible nod. Kite hitched himself a little nearer Caroline's chair.

"Three hours—that's a long time, isn't it, from Maidenhead? I believe you drive a Fiat Bertone? White, isn't it? Nippy little car."

"Yes," said Caroline, "but there was a fair amount of traffic, and you know what it's like along the A34 out of Oxford."

"Right. Not many opportunities for passing, especially if you're in a line with something slow in front. Not until you're through Stratford, that is. Traffic heavy there, as usual?"

"As usual, yes, thronged with tourists."

"I know." Kite was sympathetic. "Took me the age of a duck to get through the other day. Which way did you take?"

"Straight through. Up the main street, and on to the Evesham Road."

"Busy, was it?"

"Wood Street was chock-a-block."

"Wood Street?" repeated Kite, keenly.

"Yes, going towards the market square." She gave him a puzzled look. "It was terrible, but I wasn't in any hurry, I took my time. Then when I got to Lavenstock . . . I had a call to make."

"Where was that?" Mayo intervened.

"I called at the Pearson Secretarial Agency to see if there was any chance of them getting a quick replacement for Miss Johnson."

"What time did you get there?"

"It must have been about ten to five, I suppose. Mrs. Pearson was just packing up to go home, I remember, and I didn't stay long, certainly not more than ten minutes."

It was at times like this Caroline wished she smoked. Her hands tightened together in her lap, then consciously relaxed as she remembered the two trained observers watching her. He had grey eyes, the chief inspector, grey and steady and searching, as if he read her mind. She hoped they would put her tension down to the awful realisation that Clive would now no longer be needing another secretary, just another of the things that would now be superfluous . . . his secretary, his car, his wife . . .

"And then?"

"I had to queue to get out of the multi-storey car park—it's always busy at that time—but then I drove straight home."

"Reaching here at five-twenty." She nodded. "Mrs. Lethbridge, why did you go straight out again when you heard what had happened? I believe Constable Trenchard had requested you not to."

"Did he? I don't remember," she said vaguely. "I don't really think I knew what I was doing. I just wanted to talk to someone, and Harry is very understanding." It had been an impulse, quickly regretted; it was far better in the long run to face things alone.

"You expected him to be home at that time, before six o'clock?"

"Harry doesn't keep late office hours. It was something he and Clive disagreed about. Clive often didn't get home until eight, or even later."

While Kite noted the times, Mayo said, "Mrs. Lethbridge, this is very distressing for you, I know, but I have to ask you some rather personal questions."

"Go ahead," she said steadily.

"This house? It comes to you, now your husband is dead?"

"Brome already belongs to me. It's been in my family for generations."

"So it's unlikely you would want to sell it?"

"Sell Brome?" She looked almost insulted, making him feel as though he'd been impertinent. But then she said quietly, and more decisively than he'd yet heard her speak, "No. I would never do that."

"Do you have any private income?"

"A little, enough for my personal needs."

"Your husband was a partner in a successful architectural practice. Presumably you'll inherit his share, and that will enable you to keep the house going?" He didn't tell her, at this juncture, that amongst Lethbridge's neatly documented papers, he had already found a copy of the will, and that he knew she would come in for everything Clive had possessed.

"Yes. But a good deal of it's money that was originally my own. When we married, I made everything over to him, to buy his partnership, you know how it is." What was he getting at?

"Was your relationship with your husband a happy one, Mrs. Lethbridge?"

With both men watching her, Caroline felt her nerves exposed. It took a long time to find the courage to answer honestly, which she had to do, because others would tell him if she didn't. "Lately, we hadn't been too happy, no. There was nothing openly antagonistic, though; it was more that we became—mutually disinterested."

"You both went your own ways?"

"Clive did. I don't know that I went any way at all. For years I'd just been drifting—" She stopped, her colour heightened, and Mayo wondered whether he could have supplied the word she had bitten off. Until? Until something, or somebody, had happened to make her change her mind, and precipitate a crisis?

"There was no question of divorce?"

"We have a child, Chief Inspector, as you know . . ."

"Yes?"

"They adored each other—not that I'd have wanted it any other way. It was the best thing about Clive." Her voice shook a little. She looked down at her hands, then went on more steadily, "I sometimes thought he was in danger of spoiling her with too many expensive presents, but that was another matter. She loves us both, and it would have broken her heart if we had split up, and anyway, Clive wouldn't have given her up without a fight, and . . ." She stopped again, then said unexpectedly, "My father used to say I was by nature too disposed towards a peaceful existence, and I'm afraid he was right. Perhaps, if I'd been more positive, things might have been different."

"We all tend to blame ourselves after the event, Mrs. Lethbridge. And death especially leaves a legacy of guilt." He paused to look down at his papers, then said in quite a different tone of voice, "Do you know of anyone with reason to want your husband out of the way?"

Surprised both by the insight and the hint of something personal which had very briefly crept into his voice, the abrupt switch of direction made her blink. "Of course not!"

"No one with a grudge, an ex-employee for instance, no enemies?"

"My husband was not a very—easy man, and I suspect very few people can go through life without anyone disliking them —but," she replied in a low voice, "not enough to *kill*."

"Mr. Lethbridge had been receiving threats, however."

"Threats? I didn't know that!"

Mayo became alert. "You didn't know?"

"I mean," she explained awkwardly, "I knew he'd had anonymous letters, and calls, but I didn't know they were threatening." Yet Harry had known. Clive had told Harry— he must have done—who'd told the police. "He wouldn't talk about them. I just assumed they were the poison-pen type, you know."

"Could you say when he received the last one?"

"I don't know about the letters, but I suspect he may have received one of the calls at a party we had last week; at least he took a call which seemed to upset him."

"Was the caller a man or a woman?"

"I've no idea; I've told you he didn't discuss the matter with me."

"Except to say who he thought was behind them, of course."

"Yes. Yes, he did say that," she admitted reluctantly.

"Did you agree with him that it might be Mr. Marcus Dymond?"

"No, that was absurd. I've known him all my life, and he's not that type."

"Yet they did have a major disagreement, which apparently flared up this morning. Would you like to give me the substance of their differences?"

There was nothing she would like less, and telling of the quarrel about Oddings Cottage didn't make it any more edifying, but she made herself relate it as factually and unemotionally as possible. Like Harry, she didn't feel the need to elaborate on the fact that Clive had intended to pull down the cottage, once bought, because this would involve explanations of his plans for Brome itself, and these were, she realised with a tingle of shock that was not unpleasant, now irrelevant.

Mayo listened attentively but made no comment. "Tell me about this party, will you, please? Was it a dinner party?"

"No, no, a cocktail party, for about seventy people. It was a business arrangement, really. Clive had recently won an award, for designing a rather special holistic healing centre that's just been built in Norway, and it seemed appropriate to celebrate it that way."

"The person who killed your husband smashed the model of it, did you know?"

She looked blank. "Why should anyone do that?"

"I hoped you might be able to tell me."

"It seems a sick sort of thing to do. No one I know would do such a thing!"

"That, I'm afraid, remains to be seen. I wonder if you could let me have a list of the names and addresses of the guests at the party."

"Yes, I suppose there still is one, somewhere."

"Good. Then that's it for the moment, Mrs. Lethbridge. We'll need to check your car over, by the way. Perhaps you'd let me have the keys? A matter of routine," he assured her, seeing her frown.

"I'll let you have them right away." She stood up to go, still frowning. "That's it!" she exclaimed suddenly, "My car! When I put it in the garage tonight, I noticed something odd, but I couldn't think what it was. Clive's car wasn't there—it was being serviced today, and it should have been back."

"You garage your cars round the back of the house, don't you?"

"Yes, in the old stables. But perhaps they've brought it back since," she suggested vaguely.

Mayo raised an eyebrow at Kite, but Kite shook his head. "Hasn't been brought back since we got here."

"Was that the usual thing? For the garage to return it?" Mayo asked.

"Yes; when it needed servicing, Clive always took it in the evening before, usually on Thursdays, on his way home from work. Harry went along, too, in his own car, to drive Clive on here. It's on his way home. Then the garage would bring the car back when it was ready."

"They've probably found something that needs attention. What kind of car was it, and what garage did he use?"

"A BMW. Sanderson's, the BMW agents on Queen's Road in Lavenstock."

"We'll check it tomorrow. All right, Mrs. Lethbridge. We shall want to see you again, of course, but for the moment," he added with an unexpected kindness that nearly unmanned her, and a smile that totally changed the serious caste of his features, "try to get a good night's sleep. I'll see that my men don't disturb you."

"You're very kind," she said for what felt like the thousandth time that day.

# CHAPTER 7

"What was all that in aid of?" Mayo asked, as soon as the door had closed behind Caroline. "All that about Stratford?"

"She's lying."

Kite was looking so pleased with himself that Mayo restrained himself from saying that a child could have seen that, and waited for him to explain.

"Well, it's Stratford Mop, isn't it, this week-end?"

"It's what?"

"The Mop Fair, held every year, a big tradition. The fairground stalls and vehicles park all along the main streets while it's on, and through traffic's normally diverted. It's a right dog's breakfast, and not possible she could have come through as she said, not without being aware of it."

"Sure you've got the dates right?"

"I'm sure. We've promised to take the kids down this week-end," Kite told him, on a note of hopeful pessimism.

"Hazards of the job, lad." Apparently unmoved, Mayo was sorry for Kite's sake that a murder investigation had cropped up to spoil his plans. Letting down the family, or the wife, was an occupational hazard for policemen. He, more than most people, was aware of how much of a contributory factor this was to the breakup of a marriage. Depending on the marriage, of course. But he had no intention of rushing things at this stage—or letting Kite do so. The beginning of a case was the time to hold your horses, take things slowly and patiently, until it began to gather its own momentum.

"It might be the last chance we'll get for some time, for a family outing, I mean. It's Sheila, see. She's been accepted for that job."

Kite's wife had returned to work when their youngest had started school, considering herself lucky to be able to augment the family income by finding part-time work as a shorthand typist in the personnel department of a large engineeering works. How it had come about, Kite wasn't quite sure, but before long she was working full-time, the firm was realising her potential and Sheila was enlarging her ambitions. She was sent on courses, and began to progress so fast up the ladder that she had now been appointed assistant personnel manager.

"Great news; give her my congratulations. You must both be chuffed."

"Oh, sure, over the moon." And he was, really. "It's going to make a hole in her spare time, though. I can see us making appointments to see each other before long." Kite stuck his hands into his pockets, frowned, then shrugged. "Anyhow, that's how I'm certain about Stratford."

"It's worth following up," Mayo told him, taking the hint and not pursuing the subject of the promotion. Obviously Kite didn't know quite what had hit him yet. "Dig around and see what you can come up with, about this time Mrs. L has unaccounted for . . . unaccounted unless she *is* a very slow driver, that is."

"No way. She's been copped for speeding a couple of times to my knowledge."

"Has she, by gum? I wouldn't have thought she was the speeding type."

"Well, a car like that . . ." There was a wistful note in Kite's voice that many men would have recognised.

"Presuming she came up the motorway and got here earlier than she said, then. Could have parked in the back lane behind the orchard, nipped in and done her husband in, then driven off again—cleaned herself and her car up and come back, all innocent-like?" It could be established. There were tyre-tracks in the lane, going as far as the gate, then reversing out again, fresh after the rain of the previous night, from which casts were even now being taken.

"But is she capable of killing at all, much less bludgeoning anyone to death?" Caroline Lethbridge looked an unlikely candidate for the role of murderess, though experience taught any policeman that signified nothing. "It's my guess she's a bit of a martyr, the sort who could go on agonising for years rather than take a positive step that's likely to be painful—though we have to remember she wasn't happy with her husband, there were problems, she may even have met someone else, which could change a lot of things."

"If she was against divorce because it would upset the child so much," Kite objected, "it's hardly credible she'd choose murder as the other alternative to gaining her freedom."

"True." Yet Mayo had watched the expressions crossing her face while they spoke of Clive's death. Shocked, as anyone would have expected, by sudden death. Distressed at its violence, yes . . . worried, certainly . . . yet a real sense of loss, true sorrow, grief, or pain—where were they? Their lack lent weight to Mrs. Peach's hints about the state of the relationship between Lethbridge and his wife, but if every marriage that fell short of the ideal led to murder, Mayo thought wryly, he'd be a busy man. He needed to know more about the background before assuming that. What had he been like, Lethbridge? What manner of man had that shell of a body contained? Death had wiped the face clean—of humour, intelligence, strength or weakness, indeed, anything of the man who had in life been loved, feared, or hated.

"Have all her movements checked—what time she left these people she had lunch with . . . when she arrived at this agency, what time she left."

He sat still for a moment, frowning. "What did you make of Waring?"

"Seemed straight enough to me. Bit of a smoothie, though."

"Right. And more than a bit anxious to tell us about this row between the deceased and Dymond, wasn't he? Not like Mrs. Wharton, who seems to have seen fit to put it about there was no one here all day. I think we'd better have a word with her, and see why, before we see Marcus Dymond." It was getting very late, and he decided Dymond must wait until tomorrow morning. A devoted husband with an invalid wife, as Dymond was, according to Waring, wasn't likely to push off. "What's the set-up there?"

"With the Whartons? Both work here, as housekeeper and general handyman, with the Lodge as tied accommodation. It suits them because the husband's reading for an external degree at the university. One of those mature students." Kite paused, personal analogies intruding. Then he said, "It's my bet it was him who told Mrs. Wharton to say nothing about Dymond being here."

"Why?"

"General bloody-mindedness, I imagine. Cocky little sod, he is. The sort who's anti-police on principle. Police, and all the world agin him besides. I only saw him for a minute or two in the kitchen with his wife, but it stood out a mile that he's carrying a thumping great chip on his shoulder . . . Can't see why; he's got a pretty cushy number here, easy job, nice house. There's a lot would be grateful."

"Depends. On what price you're prepared to pay for being constantly beholden." Mayo consulted the list of names Kite had given him. "I see we've got the Whartons lined up to see next. Let's move."

Brome Lodge, just inside the main gates of Brome House, was a small house of Victorian construction, of the *cottage orné* variety, a highly desirable residence in these over-priced times, despite the pigmy-sized rooms and lack of light, which the Victorian Baddesbys had evidently considered less important than overall picturesqueness.

"Quaint, isn't it?" Kite remarked.

With its curly eaves and Gothic windows, it reminded Mayo of a Victorian money box he'd had handed down as a child, where you put your pennies down the chimney, though he'd soon found you could get them out by removing the doorstep with a knife.

Inside, laudable efforts had been made to counteract the

general subfusc claustrophobia by way of shining paintwork and light, sprigged wallpapers, with much success. Not an interior decorator's tour de force, certainly, but the effect was charming, that of a spotless doll's house. And a home for all that, where comfort wasn't sacrificed for appearances. Toys and books were scattered around, a child's drawing pinned to the wall. Janice Wharton gently smoothed into place the loose cover on the arm of her chair as she sat down, almost as if she stroked the hair of a beloved child.

After what his sergeant had said, Mayo had been half-expecting a little woman, meek and mild, but Mrs. Wharton was of average height, with strong features and heavy brows, saved from plainness by a pair of clear and beautiful hazel eyes. Her smooth, dark hair was caught back, simply, with combs. He could imagine her being under no one's thumb, though she was exceedingly pale and, at the moment, he would have sworn, under some stress. Her large, capable hands, which she endeavoured to keep folded calmly in her lap, occasionally betrayed her. Watching them unconsciously tighten, Mayo thought she was as tense as an overstrung guitar.

She answered his questions about her circumstances and the general routine of the house clearly and briefly, without adding comments of her own. As far as today went she could, she said, tell them no more than they already knew, that Clive had worked alone all day, had his meals taken to him in his study, seen no one.

"Except Mr. Marcus Dymond."

Janice Wharton did not meet his eye. A very faint colour rose in her cheeks, but she said nothing.

"Come on, Mrs. Wharton, you're not going to gain anything by not telling us everything you know. It's only going to hold things up."

"How did you find out?" she asked at last, her voice very low.

"Never mind that. Were you aware that they had a quarrel?"

"No."

Mayo knew she was lying. He said rather sharply, "We are investigating a murder, and I think we may reasonably expect a little co-operation. Think again, please."

"It was this morning when Mr. Dymond was here," she admitted at last, but still avoiding a direct answer. "Mr. Lethbridge was alive until after tea, so how could he have killed him?"

Mayo resisted the impulse to tell her it was the job of the police to make the deductions, and pointed out that Dymond could have come back later. "But of course, you would have known if he did, wouldn't you? You would have heard him and let him in, even if Mrs. Peach didn't. She's slightly deaf, isn't she?"

This long shot, based on what he'd deduced from the unnerving fixity of Mrs. Peach's stare, and her scorn of the telephone, came off.

"She is a bit, though she won't admit it. But I wasn't there this afternoon." Perhaps on surer ground now, she loosened up, became more talkative. "The arrangement is that I have the afternoons free, then go back to help with the dinner after I've picked up Nicky and Jane from school and given them their tea. Terry's usually home by then. I was able to get off early today because Mr. Lethbridge said he wanted only a light lunch, so I left him some salad and cold salmon, and a half-bottle of Montrachet in the fridge." She added, with what might have been a smile in other circumstances, "It was left-overs from dinner last night. He said he had a very busy afternoon and didn't want to be disturbed, on any account, until he rang for his tea."

"There's an internal telephone system, isn't there?"

"There has to be, in a house that size."

"And it was Mrs. Peach who made his tea?"

"She always does when she's here. Otherwise Mrs. Lethbridge, or the secretary, does it.

"Oh yes, the secretary who's just left."

"That's right," she agreed, without noticeable enthusiasm, "Miss Johnson."

"So you couldn't swear that no one visited the house this afternoon?"

She didn't reply for so long that Mayo, bringing official jargon to bear, added sternly, "Don't you want to see the culprit brought to justice?"

At that she looked up, regarding him steadily with those wide, clear hazel eyes before speaking. "Whoever killed that bastard," she said deliberately, "deserves to go free. Society should be grateful to him."

Kite looked decidedly taken aback, and even Mayo, who had become increasingly aware of a strong will, needing to be met, had hardly expected such a vehement answer.

"I'd like you to explain what you mean by that remark."

"She means," came a voice from the door, "that Mr. Clive Lethbridge was bad news, and not only for some. It'd be a lot easier to find somebody who didn't want him out the way than somebody who did."

Terry Wharton swaggered into the room, his fists deep in his pockets, and Mayo saw what Kite had meant. Wharton was a short young man in his early thirties with a mop of blond, overlong, wavy hair, and very blue eyes. There was, however, nothing in the least effeminate about him. He was wearing jeans and a black T-shirt that revealed the wide, muscular shoulders, deep chest and narrow hips of the athlete. He stood before Mayo, shifting his weight on the balls of his feet, leading with his chin, like a bantam-weight boxer waiting for the next round.

"Mr. Wharton? I'm Detective Chief Inspector Mayo, Lavenstock C.I.D., and this is Detective Sergeant Kite. We'd like to talk to you about this afternoon's events. Please sit down."

Wharton ignored the outstretched hand, declined the request. "I'll stand."

"Please sit down, Mr. Wharton, and be prepared to answer our questions," Mayo repeated, without undue emphasis, but fixing him with a look that caused Wharton to comply, and lounge into a chair with ill grace.

Mayo continued amiably, conversationally, "Don't come from round here, do you? I think I detect a fellow northerner."

"Manchester."

"Thought so. I'm from the other side of the Pennines, myself."

"Yeah?" answered Wharton, with enormous disinterest.

Mayo surveyed him thoughtfully. He probably needed all this aggression to add a few inches to his height. He said, smiling and not raising his voice, "And we don't stand for being buggered about, us Yorkshiremen, Wharton. So watch it!" Wharton blinked and sat up straighter, and Kite, who had never heard Mayo swear at a witness, thought, by God, he'd better, and hid his grin in his notebook.

"Let's have a few personal details first." They went through the business of taking name, address, age, etc. Then Mayo asked, "How long have you lived here?"

"Eighteen months, give or take a bit," Wharton said, glancing at his wife for confirmation.

"Eighteen months exactly. On the fourth of last month."

"Nice house you have."

"We've worked at it."

"It's a credit to you. You can't have much spare time. Your wife has told us of the conditions of your employment, and that you're working for an engineering degree as well."

"I manage to fit things in."

"Where were you this afternoon, Mr. Wharton?"

"Shut up in the bedroom, trying to work on an assignment."

"All afternoon? You never went out?"

"No."

Something had crept into the room, something tangible. Fear. Someone was holding their breath.

"And you never heard anything? Deep in your books, were you?"

Wharton said through his teeth, "Maybe that strikes you as funny—"

"Not in the least. Why should it?"

Mayo might have saved his breath. "It doesn't come easy to me, you know, theory. I'm all right with the practical stuff, but theory—that's another ball game. But I'm prepared to work at it, see, slave my guts out if it means a better job at the end. I took this on because I want my kids to have a better future than I had. I couldn't do what I'm doing without this job to keep me going, and this house. And my family are happy here. So if you think I murdered Lethbridge, you'd better come up with a damn good reason for me to do it."

Kite looked up from his notebook as Mayo said, "One reason could be that you had a row with Mr. Lethbridge, and lost control. It wouldn't be the first time, would it?"

There was a small sound from Wharton's wife.

"Christ, you're all alike, aren't you, you lot?" Wharton burst out. "You don't care who you pin summat like this on, as long as you get some poor bugger! Where'd you get hold of that?"

"From Mrs. Peach," said Mayo mildly.

"Mrs.—?" An odd expression crossed Wharton's face; a look passed between him and his wife, who, Mayo noted, was white as paper. Wharton gave a sudden short laugh and said, more easily, "Oh, old Peachey! You don't want to take no notice of her; she blows everything up into a big production."

Mayo went back to his original theme. "You didn't get on with your boss, though, did you?" He used the term in a deliberately provocative way, but Wharton didn't take the bait. For some reason, perhaps because he'd got something off his chest, his aggression had left him.

"No, I didn't, and I'll tell you why. Lethbridge was like a lot more, chucking his weight around because he had the upper hand, thought we should lick his boots because he'd given us this job, and he got up my nose with it, right! I've had my rows with him, and I'll admit it, but the last thing I'd be likely to do would be to cut off my bread-and-butter supply."

As they left the cottage, Mayo said, "A right one, he is. And he read into my words more than I meant, when I spoke about losing control? If he hasn't got form, I'm a monkey's uncle. Get on to it, will you?"

"All the same, she's the one who wears the pants."

And there Kite had put his finger right on the button. For all his macho image, Terry Wharton wasn't the only one to watch there. His wife was far deeper. Her attitude throughout the interview had shown she was well aware that he, Mayo, was thinking she had not only had ample opportunity, but also the capability, to commit this crime. He wondered if that was what she was afraid of, and thought again of her hands, large and strong. Her will, he suspected, was equally so. Yet all the indications were as Wharton had said, that the two of them stood to lose everything, and gain nothing, by Lethbridge's death.

# CHAPTER 8

Mayo arrived at the office by eight the following morning, ready for the briefing session with his team, culled from the Regional Crime Squad, which would begin the day. He found Kite already there, a large bacon sandwich in his fist, and a pint mug of coffee steaming on the desk beside him.

"Didn't your mother ever tell you all that coffee'll rot your socks?"

"Give over, got to have something to bring me to the surface! We didn't get much sleep last night, remember—besides, I don't drink all that much, do I?"

"I suppose we should be thankful it's not beer."

"What, on my salary?"

"Stir yourself and let's be having some evidence you're worth that much."

But Kite, despite not having rolled into bed until dawn, must have been in the office for some time. He'd already submitted his reports, in his execrable typing. Before the session, he and Mayo went through the case with Garvey, the allocating sergeant, and Backhouse, the detective inspector in charge of the incident room, which was already alive with both plain-clothes and uniformed men and women, video screens flashing, telephones and typewriters going. Whenever possible, Mayo set his incident room where such facilities were easily accessible, as in this case, with the murder location within striking distance.

"Detail somebody to go through Lethbridge's office in Birmingham this morning, will you, Sergeant?" he asked Garvey.

"Inspector Atkins?" Mayo nodded. Atkins, an inspector for

twelve years and aspiring to nothing higher, preferring to work under instruction rather than use his own initiative, was tireless over humdrum, routine work. Phenomenal in his local knowledge, stubborn as a mule, therein lay his strength.

Before he left, Mayo buttonholed Kite. "I've got the P.M. at eleven, so that leaves me just about time to see Dymond first, but I want you over at Brome. You know the drill. Get the door-to-door finished, see whether anybody noticed a car parked in the lane, or anything unusual. If they've finished with the study, get Mrs. Peach to take a look and see if anything's missing—Mrs. Lethbridge as well, of course, though I'll be surprised if it is. And don't forget her car. Looks like I'm lumbered with Deeley this morning. Ah well, I reckon it's time he was made to justify his existence."

"Better get off right away, then. I'll see you back here?"

"No, wait, we'll drop you at the house on the way to Dymond's. No sense in taking two cars, even if you're not paying for the petrol. Come back when you're ready in one of the squad cars; they'll be to-ing and fro-ing all morning."

Spoken like a true Yorkshireman, Kite thought, but didn't quite dare say it.

Earlier that morning the bright sun, concentrated through a chink in the drawn curtains, shone on to Matt Royston's face, waking him five minutes before the telephone at the bedside rang. He had worked late the previous night, successfully shutting out everything else, but his thoughts this morning could not be so easily controlled. Clive had promised him free access to all sketches, plans and notes which had charted the progress of the Svensen Centre, but now . . . Matt faced his own attitudes with some ambivalence.

The telephone rang, startling him. Looking at his watch as he reached out for it, he saw it wasn't yet seven.

"Waring here," announced the caller. "Harry Waring."

Waring? "I was about to ring you today to fix that appointment we spoke about. Looks as though you've beaten me to it."

"Oh, that!" Waring gave a short, nervous laugh. "Better forget it; it doesn't matter now. Look, I'm sorry to disturb you at this hour, but I know you were due to meet my partner over this book of yours this morning . . ." Waring paused. "I have to tell you that something very shocking has happened . . ."

Matt sat on the bed, his hand still resting on the receiver after Waring had rung off, staring at the shaft of sunlight on the carpet. Lethbridge, dead. Irrevocably, incontrovertibly dead. He found to his surprise that he was sweating, and his hands were not quite steady. Caroline. He must see Caroline. Immediately.

He showered, dressed, then took time to have breakfast in the dining room when he realised she might not be ready to see him just yet—Waring had spoken of sleeping pills—if indeed she was willing to see him at all. He would have understood that, in the circumstances.

Yet the bizarreness of what had happened only really hit him when he was let though the gates by a uniformed constable, and then given the once-over by a plain-clothes man in the house before being allowed to see Caroline, who was, he was told, in the drawing room.

They faced each other, awkwardly, divided more by Clive dead than Clive living. Matt felt that anything he said was likely to be wrong, and he guessed Caroline probably had similar hesitations. There were shadows like bruises under her eyes. She took refuge in offering him coffee from a heated jug that was standing plugged in on a side table, coffee that had stood too long and was bitter and black. He noticed that though she had poured one for herself, she forgot it and left it on the table. She walked to the fireplace, where she stood leaning her elbow on the stone mantel and looking down into a copper urn massed with dahlias in fiery tones of orange and red that had been set into the empty grate.

"Caroline, I—"

"Don't, please. There's nothing to say now, is there?" Her

voice was cold and formal. "It was kind of you to come," she added, as though he was the vicar offering routine condolences, as though yesterday afternoon, and what they had planned together, had never happened, or meant nothing to her.

Oh, Christ! This wasn't going to get them anywhere. He could understand the awkwardness of the moment, that physical contact between them might seem inappropriate to her at this moment, distasteful, even an obscenity; he could understand that she might be feeling guilty by association, because he was in fact busy coping with a fair-sized portion of self-disgust on his own behalf. His first thought on hearing that Clive was actually *dead* had been, well, whatever comes of it, that's one problem solved.

Caroline spoke unexpectedly, on a soft, prolonged sigh, as if she had tuned in to his wavelength, and seen the futility of trying to keep up a barrier between them. "Do you believe that if you want something passionately enough, you can make it happen, Matt? If I hadn't wanted so desperately to be free of Clive—"

"No," he interrupted roughly, "I don't."

"No. I don't know why I said that, I don't believe it either, not really; that sort of thinking is just being self-indulgent . . ." She stopped herself abruptly, her eyes huge. "It was such a pointless thing to have done, after all."

"Whatever else, murder isn't often pointless. Is it, Caroline?"

"Oh, Matt!"

They stood looking at one another, facing the enormity of what had been done.

"The police think it was somebody who knew him," she said at last, "maybe somebody connected with this house, and . . . oh God, I've done such a stupid thing; I told them a lie, and I think that sergeant spotted it. I'd forgotten about the Mop Fair . . ."

When she had finished telling him what she had said to the

police, he looked at her steadily, saying quietly, "You didn't want them to know you'd spent an hour with me. Why?"

"Why? Don't you see? Won't that make them realise we might have had a reason, an opportunity—for, for murdering Clive?"

The silence didn't last very long, but to Caroline it seemed to stretch out between them like an elastic band being pulled to its limits.

"But we didn't," he said at last, deliberately, "did we?" And crossed the space between them in one stride.

"There's also the question of the book," he said later. "Do you still want to go ahead with it?"

"Why not? If it's possible, that is. Clive was so—*triumphant* at being included, you know. It would seem the least we can do."

"Then I will, if *you* want it. I know he'd finished getting together all his notes and sketches, and he had my main outline, which he'd commented on and was going to return to me this morning when he handed over his notes. I must have both sets of papers, but otherwise there's no problem."

"You'll have to ask the police. I daresay they'll be with all his other papers, in the study, but they've locked it up."

The senior detectives in charge of the case wouldn't be here until later, the young plain-clothes man he'd spoken to before told him, and he was sorry, it was outwith his responsibility to let Matt into the study, or the secretary's room.

"I don't need to go in. It's only a file I need."

The detective constable was an urbanely smiling young man called Farrar, a neat dresser, with smooth, fair hair and sharp blue eyes. Forensic had finished with both rooms, and last night he and the chief inspector had spent a couple of hours going through the desk and filing cabinets. Mayo had taken away anything he considered important, but it was more than Farrar cared to risk, letting anyone in without the gaffer's say-so. "I'm sorry, sir, I can't let you have it, not

without Mr. Mayo gives permission. He or Sergeant Kite.
Either of them should be here shortly."

"It's my own property, a blue manilla file, clearly marked
with my own name."

"Makes no difference, sir, and in any case, I don't recall
such a file—and I was the one who listed the contents of the
desks and filing cabinets."

"You must be mistaken."

"No, sir." Detective Constable Farrar was no longer smiling. And he was quite evidently not to be moved from his
position.

"Maybe it's up at the office," Caroline suggested. "It's not
likely to be anywhere else in the house. Clive was always very
careful not to leave anything to do with his work lying
around, but I'll have a look, if you like."

She seemed glad to have even this small thing to occupy
her, and left Matt to try his luck on the telephone to Waring
& Lethbridge. There was, as he'd hoped, someone there. A
Mrs. Endicott, Harry Waring's secretary, a woman speaking
in a consciously modulated voice, albeit with iron-grey over-
tones, who made the conventional shocked noises about the
death, then told him that a police inspector called Atkins was
already there, going through Lethbridge's office. "As if all
this wasn't upsetting enough," she said, touchily, "they want
to lock up all his papers and files; it's really very inconvenient
for Mr. Waring."

She had been with the inspector, showing him where any
relevant material was kept, she said, managing to convey that
she held him directly responsible for her interrupted week-
end, and she was absolutely certain that neither Matt's own
manuscript, nor Clive's notes on it, had been there, in a blue
manilla folder or anywhere else. Matt believed her.

"Miss Johnson would have known where they were, but of
course, she's in America now, isn't she?"

"Yes, I believe so, but that's a thought, all the same. It
might be worth a telephone call," said Matt, to whom tele-

phone calls halfway across the world were routine. "Would it be too much trouble to ask you for her address there?"

"Not at all. Give me a few minutes and I'll ring you back."

She was back within five minutes, sounding flustered. "I'm sorry, but it doesn't appear that she left a forwarding address. There's no reason why she should, of course, officially, and she wasn't personally on terms with any of the girls to correspond with them."

Matt thought for a moment, then said, "Let me have her home address, here, if you will. They'll be sure to know."

There was a small silence at the other end. "The thing is," announced Mrs. Endicott unhappily, "we don't appear to have that, either."

"Isn't that rather unusual?"

"It's unheard of, I assure you, in *this* office! However, Miss Johnson wasn't set on through the usual channels—Mr. Lethbridge himself engaged her, quite irregularly, only five or six weeks since, presumably through some employment agency, though we haven't had any invoices for her services as yet."

And that was what came of bypassing the official channels, her voice said. Matt thanked her for her trouble and rang off.

Caroline had had no luck, either, but when he told her of his conversation with Mrs. Endicott, she said immediately, "It wasn't through an agency that Clive got hold of Sylvia; it was through Amanda."

"Amanda?"

"Amanda Bradford, his previous secretary—his permanent one, really. She's on maternity leave at the moment, and recommended Sylvia as a temporary replacement."

"Bradford? I remember the name . . . She was the one I dealt with when we made the first approaches to Clive about the book. Okay," Matt said, "what's her number?"

It seemed inevitable, given the other frustrations of the morning, that the number should be out of order.

"I suppose nobody knows her address, either?" he asked Caroline with resignation.

"Of course I do; she lives over at Hinton."

# CHAPTER 9

Detective Constable Pete Deeley turned the police car left, off the Lavenstock road, conscious of the chief inspector's eyes on the back of his neck, and therefore mindful of police driving school techniques. Sergeant Kite, announcing that Deeley's driving made him seasick if he sat in the back, had opted for the passenger seat beside Deeley, but the gaffer was in an unusually talkative mood. Consequently, Kite's seat-belt making it difficult for him to carry on the conversation without turning round, he had to twist his neck every time an answer was required. Deeley grinned to himself.

"What do we know about Dymond," Mayo wondered aloud, "other than this feud that seems to have existed between him and Lethbridge? Didn't he used to be a maths master at the old grammar school?"

"Search me," Kite said.

"I know him a bit, sir," Deeley put in diffidently. "Or I used to—he taught me at one time."

"*You?*" Kite uttered with unflattering amazement, which the other two rightly ignored, Mayo because he knew there must, contrary to all appearances, be more to Deeley than appeared on the surface. The powers that be who'd selected him for C.I.D. couldn't be complete fools.

"What did you think of him, Deeley?" he asked the constable, with interest.

"We hated him—sadistic bastard, he was, sir. Most of us, anyway. Some swore by him—the high-flyers, the ones he got through to Oxbridge. I believe," Deeley said, struggling to be fair, "he was reckoned a good teacher, for such as them. He'd no patience with the hoi polloi, only spoke to us to put us down. No wonder Lethbridge hated him."

"Your prejudices are showing," Mayo commented, mildly amused but interested in this, the longest speech he'd ever heard from the inarticulate Deeley, who played a formidable wing three-quarter in the divisional rugby team, but was not otherwise noted for his prowess. "Let's see what you make of him now."

"You won't want me to come in with you, will you, sir?" Deeley's agony was acute.

"You'll learn nothing sitting in the car with your nose in page three, lad."

"He won't remember you, now you've grown your feathers," Kite grinned.

Deeley's hand went defensively to the full, silky moustache he'd recently begun to sprout. His face assumed a look of martyred endurance, and he said nothing more.

They dropped Kite at the entrance gates of Brome, where a uniformed constable stood on guard. Mayo leaned out of the car and called after Kite, "If they haven't already done so, get this lane checked out as far as the Lavenstock road, okay?"

Kite stuck up a thumb. "Will do."

They drove back through Brome village, on to the Lavenstock Road and up the further slope of the valley. Russell Road, when they eventually found it, was an unmade road, and the house they sought was one of half a dozen largish properties, mostly mock-Tudor style with steeply sloping roofs and gables. All of them were fronted with well-kept gardens, not least the one they were interested in, which had a sweep of velvet lawn setting off a profusion of unusual plants and flowers, beautifully tended and perfectly grown.

A woman in a wheelchair was very slowly and with evident difficulty clipping a too enthusiastic spray from a luxuriously rampant climbing rose, using long-handled secateurs. Difficult as it was, she appeared to be coping admirably. When she saw them approaching, she abandoned the task and leaned the secateurs against the wall, removing her gardening gloves.

"Good morning. You must be the police; I'm Enid Dymond," she greeted them composedly when they reached her, extending a hand which Mayo found as light and insubstantial as a bird's claw. "Lovely weather, isn't it?" Mayo introduced himself and Deeley. "My husband is expecting you, Chief Inspector," she went on, as calmly as if they had called to read the gas meter. "Just ring, will you? Marcus is out at the back, but we have a garden extension bell, so he'll hear you."

Deeley stepped forward and pressed the bell, while Mayo remarked, "He's expecting us?"

"Well, yes. It's about poor Caroline's husband, isn't it? Dr. Ison made his usual visit to me just after he'd been called out there to Brome—what dreadful things our doctors have to do! And since Marcus was there at Brome yesterday also, we assumed you'd wish to see him. Poor Caroline, and poor little Pippa!"

Mayo noted that Mrs. Dymond gave no evidence of being unduly worried about her husband's involvement in a murder enquiry. The confidence of innocence? And though apparently a compassionate woman, her regrets were for Caroline Lethbridge and the child only. He wondered briefly whether anyone at all was sorry for the poor devil whose life had been so suddenly terminated.

Marcus Dymond appeared to be in no hurry to receive them, and to bridge an awkward gap while they waited, Mayo commented on the garden, asking the name of the climber Mrs. Dymond had been snipping at. Her face came alight; she touched one of the white petals lovingly. "Ah, isn't it a beauty? It's Kiftsgate—its only fault is that it's so exuberant. It must never be allowed to get out of hand, otherwise it takes over, and then tends to grow very shapeless as it grows older—rather like the rest of us, hm?"

Mayo had expected to be hampered by interviewing a probable murder suspect in front of his frail, white-faced invalid

wife, had indeed been half-prepared to insist that the interview be conducted privately, so that he was now greatly relieved to see that this would most probably not be necessary.
Enid Dymond might indeed be frail in body, but he was prepared to believe her mind and intelligence as robust as the
next. She somehow still contrived to look elegant rather than
thin; the gauntness of her face was mitigated by a discreet
and careful make-up, her hair was neatly arranged and her
clothes becoming. Her mouth was humorous; only her eyes
gave her away. Mayo had seen that look before; with pity, he
recognised what it meant.

At that moment, Marcus Dymond came to the door. A tall,
lean man with a bitter face, hollowed cheeks and an unyield-
ing mouth, a face straight from the illustrations in a medieval
history book, the closed face of a monk or a martyr. Once
more introductions were made. "Deeley," the man repeated,
dry and precise, when it came to the young constable's turn.
"Peter Deeley. How many years since I taught, or attempted
to teach, you?" His eyes rested unerringly on Deeley's sunset-
hued tie and tightly-filled suit.

"Nine or ten, sir."

"All was not lost, it seems. One's faith in the value of our
education system is restored to see Deeley upholding the
forces of law and order."

"Yes, sir," answered Deeley, his face wooden.

"I think you know why we're here, sir; shall we go inside?"
Mayo intervened, somewhat shortly.

Marcus Dymond turned and, pushing his wife's wheelchair
ahead of him, led the way through the hall into a room at the
back, where a wide window with a french door overlooked
the garden at the rear. Even Mayo, who was no gardener, felt
the sheer delight of the subtle blending of plants and shrubs,
colour and form. Near the house, where the ground was
level, not a weed was visible, every plant and flower flour-
ished voluptuously; it was only farther away, where the
ground began to slope, gently at first, then more steeply away
from the house, apparently in a series of terraces, that traces

of neglect could be discerned in the plumes of uncut grass
and unstaked plants.

"It's large," the other man remarked, seeing his interest.
"Over an acre in all. Fortunately, we can close our eyes to its
present shortcomings, since one can in fact see comparatively
little of it from here. But it really needs someone younger to
take it over."

In the look that he exchanged with his wife, Mayo saw that
Dymond had not yet accepted that his wife had passed beyond the point at which it mattered greatly, but that she allowed the fiction to continue. To admit otherwise would be
to admit that she had given up hope.

"You'll have some coffee?" Mrs. Dymond asked. "It won't
take long to make."

"Thank you, no, we've just had some." They seated themselves in the chairs Dymond waved them to. A comfortable
room, its furnishings obviously unchanged for many years,
its design, like the house itself, popular in the 1930s—mock-
oak ceiling beams, oak studding on the white plastered walls,
a mirrored overmantel and a plate rack bearing a fine collection of blue and white Delft. Polished boards surrounded a
carpet square, and in the ingle-nook were two deeply comfortable leather club armchairs, rather the worse for wear,
which Mayo, sitting in one of them, irrationally and immediately coveted.

Deeley's interest, however, was concentrated only on one
part of the room, where on an upright piano a group of
signed photographs was arranged. Ex-pupils at degree cere-
monies, self-conscious in new academic regalia, groups taken
at school functions. In none of them did Deeley himself feature. But he could recognise a few of his fellow pupils—An-
derson, captain of games in his own last year . . . and that
one, what was his name, the boy wonder, Simon something
or other . . . and the Davenport twins . . .

The chief inspector's voice brought Deeley back to now.
Hastily he sought notebook and biro. He was going to need
all his concentration.

"Mr. Dymond, we're here to make enquiries about the sudden death of Mr. Clive Lethbridge, and I'd like to start by asking you what the purpose of your visit to him yesterday was, at his home."

Dymond laughed shortly. "It wasn't simply a friendly call, as I suppose you've gathered."

"I understand you had high words."

"We did indeed. Alas, it's no secret that I was on bad terms with Lethbridge. It goes back a long way—"

"Marcus, please don't upset yourself."

"My dear, I've long since ceased to allow it to do that!" The harsh lines of Dymond's face relaxed as he smiled at his wife. "Though I never could stand the fellow—and the feeling was mutual. To be frank, we couldn't meet for five minutes without putting each other's backs up, so I kept out of his way."

"On this occasion, however, you sought him out, and the ensuing quarrel was quite violent."

"On this occasion, Chief Inspector, he had gone too far, even for Clive Lethbridge."

"In what connection?"

Dymond stood up and walked to the mantel, picked up the pipe that was lying there and shoved it in his mouth. He didn't light it, however, and after a moment he took it out, gesturing towards the window with the stem. "Observe the bone of contention."

Mayo raised his eyebrows questioningly.

"The cottage straight across from here, standing on that small plateau just below Brome House on the crest of the opposite hill."

Just visible was a long, low building, black and white, with a red pantiled roof, backed by trees. On the skyline, the upper half of Brome House and its red roofs and tall, twisted chimneys could be seen.

"Oddings Cottage," went on Dymond, "for which, some months ago, Lethbridge severely overbid. He paid a quite ridiculous sum for it, but the general opinion was that even after restoring it, he could expect to resell and still make a fairly substantial profit. Odious, but understandable in a man of Lethbridge's type. I learned yesterday, however, that he had applied for a contravention of the preservation order, intending to pull the whole thing down and build a new, modern-style house."

"Use those binoculars and you'll see why we were so angry," Mrs. Dymond added.

Mayo put the binoculars lying on the window sill to his eyes and focused the powerful lenses. The cottage then sprang into sharp relief, but without the glasses, it had been unobtrusive enough. A modern house equally, however avant-garde, would surely be unobjectionable at this distance, but in such cases, between the conservationist lobby and the modernists, feelings were apt to run high . . . In this case, there was added provocation. "I believe you also made a bid for the cottage when it was put on the market?"

"If you know that, then you'll know what my principal differences with Lethbridge were. Yesterday I made my position quite clear, which was that I would stop him with any means in my power. Then, since I had no more to say, I left, and," he added dryly, "I didn't go back again."

Mayo said blandly, "I take it that means you can substantiate your whereabouts during the late afternoon."

Dymond took the pipe, which he had neither filled nor lit yet, from his mouth and knocked it against the brick of the fireplace. "Actually, no. I was here, pottering about the garden, but I've no witnesses to the fact."

Enid Dymond said, "But don't you remember, Marcus? I was resting," she told Mayo, "and he brought me a cup of tea up at four."

Mayo intercepted their quick exchange of glances . . . thanks on his part? On hers, a kind of defiance? Certainly a barely perceptible shake of Dymond's head as he smiled at his wife. A transforming, almost boyish smile, wiping his features clean of their sardonic expression for a brief moment. Then he said, "More to the point, I made a telephone call, which I assume could be verified."

"At what time?"

"Half past four, after I'd had my own tea."

"The call was made to—?"

"Waring. Mr. Harry Waring, Lethbridge's partner."

This confirmed Waring's statement, and assuming both were telling the truth, it put both of them in the clear at the time of the murder. "What did you speak to him about?"

"I wanted to know what Lethbridge was up to. If he was going to take Caroline and young Pippa to live in this monstrosity he planned to build on the Oddings Cottage site, which was what he told me he intended, what was going to happen to Brome House? I quite violently disliked the thought of a modern housing estate up there on the hill in its place."

"So that was what he was planning?"

"No. It wasn't, as it happens, but something equally barbaric was being mooted, from any thinking person's point of view. Nevertheless, I was actually quite relieved when I learned from Waring what it was, simply because I could not see Caroline ever being a party to such absolute desecration. He was actually planning to turn that beautiful house into what he called a suite of prestige offices. Sheer vandalism! Not, of course, that that would have worried him."

But who else might it have worried? Dymond himself? Yes. Caroline Lethbridge, perhaps. Hm. Mayo put the question aside for the moment. "What kind of car do you drive, Mr. Dymond?"

"A Mini." So that was out; the tyre-tracks found in the lane indicated a wider wheelbase. He stood up. "Before I go, I'd like a specimen of your handwriting, please." Dymond wasn't to know that they possessed no copies of the anonymous letters, that they didn't even know whether they'd been handwritten or not. Mayo thought it unlikely, given the sort of man Dymond was, that the request would provoke a reaction; he was too intelligent for that. All the same, it was worth a try.

"My *handwriting?* Don't you mean my fingerprints?"

"Those, too," Mayo said.

"May I ask why—why the handwriting?"

Dymond seemed to be suppressing some inner amusement as he reached for a biro off the mantelshelf, but the look changed when Mayo said, "You didn't know Mr. Lethbridge had been receiving anonymous letters?"

The other's astonishment at this appeared genuine, but it was momentary. "That's a most offensive accusation."

"I made no accusation, sir, offensive or otherwise."

"Not offensive, to suggest that I would stoop to such juvenile behaviour?"

Mayo thought, God, he's actually less concerned about being accused of murder than writing anonymous letters! Or maybe—that's what he meant Mayo to think. A complicated man, Marcus Dymond, a man of secret thoughts.

# CHAPTER 10

Wykefield Close, Hinton, was a desirable address by Lavenstock standards, whose citizens were of the general opinion that the houses must be good if they cost that much. Hinton itself was a village recently expanded by the building of a large private housing estate and a shopping precinct, until it now touched the edges of the town. There were three main varieties of house: the "Regent," a four-bedroom Georgian style; the "California," a three-bedroom bungalow; and the "Lausanne," a four-bedroom chalet style. All were detached, if only just.

The Bradfords occupied a Californian bungalow on a corner plot, and though it couldn't have been more than two or three years old, the garden that encircled it already looked thoroughly well established. Instant gardening by means of pot-grown shrubs and trees bought at one of the new garden centres, Matt thought as he rang the bell.

A young woman in late pregnancy opened the door, and Matt introduced himself, apologising for not making an appointment, explaining that her telephone was out of order.

Amanda Bradford told him that she had already reported it. "I thought, in fact, you were the repairman."

She remembered his name and, recalling the correspondence about Clive's collaboration on the book, had no hesitation about asking him in, showing him into a large, specklessly tidy L-shaped room, which reminded him of the faultless letters she had sent him . . . she herself, for she had been that kind of secretary.

She offered him coffee, and while she was preparing it, he looked round the large room, furnished pleasantly, though

without much originality, like something lifted from the
Ideal Homes Exhibition. Ruffled Austrian blinds at the windows, oyster-coloured velvet three-piece suite, expensive
wallpaper and a reproduction Regency dining set occupying
the foot of the L. An imitation gas coal fire whose contours
never changed, nor fell into troublesome ash, was set in the
Adam-style grate. All organised to a T, the housework already done and Ms. Bradford, used to the rush and bustle of a
busy office, bored enough to be pleased to have someone to
talk to.

Matt, who knew nothing of pregnant women's susceptibili-
ties, was just realising that he was going to have to be the
imparter of some shocking news, and he waited until he had
taken the coffee tray from her and placed it on a table before
he told her, somewhat warily, what had happened. She was
visibly shaken. "Clive Lethbridge? Murdered? But that's terrible!"

"You liked Mr. Lethbridge?" Matt was surprised to see her
feel for a chair as though her legs would no longer hold her.
Nice legs, with ankles still slim and neat, despite her ad-
vanced pregnancy. She was very attractive altogether, in fact,
her make-up immaculate, her hair a silken bell of light
brown. She was well into her thirties, Matt surmised,
recognising the now familiar phenomenon of the career
woman whose child-bearing was briskly fitted into her sched-
ule.

"I worked for him for nearly eight years. No, I wouldn't
say I was over-fond of him; he could be very difficult indeed
to work for, but still . . . I had hoped to go back, after the
baby . . . His present secretary was only temporary, you
know."

"Sylvia Johnson," Matt said, wondering which had jolted
her most, the fact of Clive's murder or the sudden termina-
tion of her career prospects.

"That's right. You'll have met her, of course."

"Actually, she's the reason I'm here . . . I'm trying to find
the address she's gone to in Boston."

"Boston, America? Sylvia's in America? I didn't know that! What's she doing there?" Amanda was plainly astonished. "Has someone else replaced her?" she added rather quickly.

"No, not yet," Matt told her, answering the last question first. "Sylvia has an aunt in Boston, who's found her a job. She flew there only yesterday, and since some papers I need can't be found, I had the idea a telephone call to her might establish their whereabouts. But if you don't know her address in the States, perhaps her people here can give it me—if I can contact them. The office don't seem to have had her home address, however."

Amanda frowned. "They don't? How very odd. Well, I'm sorry, but I don't know it, either."

"Hm, that's awkward. I assumed, when Mrs. Lethbridge said you were a friend of hers, that you would. You were the one who recommended her to work for her husband?"

"Yes, I was, and I believe he was very satisfied."

"So I've gathered."

Amanda busied herself for a while by pouring more coffee for them both. "Mind you, once or twice at the beginning, I had a few doubts about that, so I rang and asked him how she was getting on, but he spoke so glowingly about her, I knew it was all right, after all."

"Why should you have doubts?"

"Well, you see, I didn't actually know her very well at all." She bit her lip. "It was funny, really, how I met her. It was one evening last winter, I'd called at Sainsbury's on my way home from work, on their late shopping night; there's one in the new shopping precinct here . . . Anyway, just as I came out of the door, we collided with one another, one of my shopping bags was knocked from my hand and everything went all over the place. She was terribly embarrassed and helped me to pick them up and carry them to the car. We were ages getting things sorted out—a jar of jam had broken and a flour bag burst; you can imagine what a mess there was. It took us so long she missed her bus, so the least I could do was to offer to run her home, but she wouldn't hear of it. Her next bus wasn't for nearly half an hour, so I suggested she came home and had a cup of coffee with me while she waited. And that's how it was."

"You struck up a rapport?"

Amanda hesitated. "Not—exactly. Sylvia was a bit of a funny girl, really. At first I thought she might just have been lonely. I told her to pop around any time she felt like it, and she took me up on that . . . People don't always, do they?"

Matt had the impression Amanda had not been altogether too thrilled about it, either, but it was an impression she sought to dispel very quickly. "I mean, I didn't mind, as long as she gave me a ring first. My husband's job takes him away quite a bit, so I'm often on my own, but I do have other friends I like to see regularly."

Matt nodded, mildly amused at the thought of Amanda's friends being allowed their allotted time. "What do you mean, a funny girl? Did she make a nuisance of herself?"

"Oh gosh, no, but she was—well, secretive. She never invited me back to her place; I don't even know where it was, except that she always got a number ten bus . . . To tell you the truth, we hadn't an awful lot in common, but I felt sorry for her; she didn't seem to have any family or friends. I knew her qualifications were excellent, though, and I thought I could help her a bit by mentioning her name when I was ready to leave."

She glanced quickly at Matt and must have thought she hadn't impressed him very much with her reasons for thinking Sylvia slightly odd, because she said, "Another thing, she was a member of one of those queer sects. I don't remember the name . . . She only mentioned it once, because I think she saw I hadn't got much time for that sort of thing. She didn't push it down your throat, like some of them do, I'll give her that . . . Oh, hang on a minute."

She raised herself awkwardly from her low chair and went to a drawer set in a large wall fitment, returning with something which she held out on her palm. It was a small gilded brooch, or rather a badge, apparently made up of intertwined initials, though what they were, it was impossible to tell at first glance.

"I think this may have been something to do with her religion; at any rate, she always wore it, and she wasn't one for jewellery or anything like that, not even make-up, though she could have been quite attractive—as it was, she couldn't have made herself look worse if she'd tried."

Sylvia Johnson had been so neglible, so nondescript, without a modicum of originality, that Matt found it almost impossible to recall what she'd looked like.

"I did try to get her to take an interest in herself, but she just didn't want to know; perhaps it was against her principles or something." Amanda shrugged. "Anyway, if you look at the back of this, you'll see the pin's broken. I found it the last time she'd been here."

"Do you mind if I borrow it?"

"Keep it, if you want," Amanda said indifferently. "It's no good to me; then when you do contact Sylvia, she can have it back."

Matt drove back to Brome House in a very thoughtful frame of mind.

# CHAPTER 11

Post-mortems were ordeals with which familiarity bred neither contempt nor congeniality. Mayo got through by regarding them as a necessary evil, occasions to endure. They were always over, eventually. The pathologist, Timpson-Ludgate, confirmed Ison's findings, that death was due to the injuries resulting from multiple blows to the skull. Examination of the stomach contents indicated that death had occurred between four and four-thirty.

Mayo left his car parked in the forecourt of the new building that was the divisional headquarters in Lavenstock. He'd never before looked at the building objectively: only now did he realise, with a shock, how ugly its brick and concrete structure was and, though he was no judge, how far from any architectural merit it must be. He wondered why—why couldn't function equate with agreeableness, as it apparently had in the Centre Lethbridge had designed? The photographs he'd seen had shown a pleasing, harmonious group—different, unexpected, but not jarring, even to untutored eyes. Yet someone had disliked it enough to perpetrate a senseless act of vandalism on the model. Or had that simply been a further extension of the hatred vented on Lethbridge himself?

As he walked into the entrance Evans, the sergeant who'd tyrannised over the desk for the last twelve years, a law unto himself, called him over. "The man everybody's looking for! Press wanting a statement, TV after you to be on the box tonight, and the super wanting to see you about it when you've a minute." His lugubrious face split into a faint grin. "I dunno, just like a bloomin' pop star! You want an agent, just let me know; I'm available from next week."

"Oh aye, sitting with your feet up, lucky devil, pitying us poor slobs who still have to work."

"Don't know so much about that, with all the jobs our Iris has lined up." Evans' face looked more like a bloodhound than ever. "Retirement! Sooner be working, I would."

"Get away with you! We'll miss your smiling face, though. Seeing Mallin there won't be the same. Okay, tell the super I'm on my way—and get them to send some sandwiches and coffee up to my office in about half an hour, will you, Taff? Owt'll do—cheese for preference."

"By the way," Evans called after him, "we've got a replacement coming down from your old division, name of Jones. Sergeant Jones."

"Jones? Must have been after my time; I don't recall any Sergeant Jones."

"Case of promotion, I think." Evans licked his thumb and turned a page. "Sergeant Jones was a W.P.C. before. Wonder if she's Welsh."

"What's her first name?"

"Alexandra Elizabeth," Evans read from the notes, pulling his mouth down. "There's posh! Let's hope she gets Sandra, or Liz."

"Wrong on all counts. She's not Welsh, but she's a nice girl in spite of it, and no side to her, either. And she's called Alex."

Eschewing the lifts, Mayo began to climb the stairs, a small daily discipline he imposed on himself, never quite sure whether he did so because Doc Ison maintained it was good for the heart, or because of the sense of virtue thus accrued. Alex, eh? Now, there was a turn-up for the book, sergeant and all, though nobody deserved promotion more. Thoroughly reliable, cheerful, sensible, and a good-looker into the bargain. He wondered why she'd transferred here.

"Come in, Gil, sit you down."

Superintendent Howard Cherry and Mayo were old friends. They had started together many years ago, round about the same time, in the old West Riding Constabulary, and when Mayo had made his application for a transfer and been offered Lavenstock, the fact that Cherry would be his superintendent had been a deciding factor in his acceptance. He was a man comfortable to work with, who didn't breathe down your neck too heavily, as long as you kept him fed with the necessary information.

They discussed the press release, decided Cherry would do the TV bit, then Cherry asked, "Any leads yet?"

Mayo said cautiously, "Not the usual domestic squabble, I can tell you that."

Cherry raised disciplined eyebrows. He looked like a well-brushed civil servant, a tall, impeccable man whose urbanity concealed an open, shrewd and agile mind. He knew, as well as Mayo, that the majority of murders were solved before the corpse was cold, the weapon practically still in the hands of the murderer, someone pushed beyond the limits of endurance, stunned and appalled at a situation that had run so suddenly out of control. "No suspects?"

"Trouble is, *everybody* seemed to hate his guts. Nearest suspect we've got at the moment's a chap I interviewed this morning, name of Marcus Dymond, and he's debatable."

"Marcus Dymond?" Cherry echoed. "Retired schoolmaster? But he taught my eldest lad!" He registered Mayo's expression and grinned ruefully. "All right, carry on."

As succinctly as he could, Mayo reviewed the case so far. Cherry listened attentively. He made no notes, but Mayo knew he would remember everything, right down to the fine details. When he'd finished, Cherry said, "Well, see how you go—but stick to the book with this one, Gil. Play it carefully. These aren't the sort of people we can afford to upset."

Mayo had time to make a few telephone calls and a quick scan of the papers he'd gathered up on his way in before his sandwiches arrived. They were very good, wholemeal bread and not too much pickle. Kite came in just as he wiped the last crumbs from his mouth.

Atkins had apparently found nothing of any relevance in Lethbridge's office. Nor had the house-to-house enquiries in

Brome village revealed anything, though they were still in-
complete, Saturday morning being the worst possible time to
catch people at home. Half the village seemed to have taken
themselves over to Lavenstock, to shop or pursue various
weekend activities. Kite's investigations into the non-return
of the BMW, however, had opened up a new line of enquiry.

"The garage people did take it back to Brome House on
Thursday afternoon, about half past three, as arranged. One
of the lads drove it, with another behind him in the garage
runabout to take him back. Lethbridge apparently saw them
coming up the drive and stopped them outside the study as
they were driving it towards the back. Told them to leave it
where it was with the keys in, as he might need it shortly.
And that's the last anybody's seen of it. Mrs. Peach confirms
seeing it there, though she didn't hear it arrive, or hear it
being driven away, though she probably wouldn't, being
hard of hearing."

"What about the Whartons? They're not deaf—either of
them see or hear the car go past?"

"Apparently not, but both the bedroom, where Wharton
was working, and the kitchen, where Mrs. W was doing some
ironing, are at the back of the Lodge. Maybe Lethbridge actually did take his car out, and left it somewhere, though it
seems unlikely, and it wouldn't give him time to get far—and
to come back—in time to get himself murdered by half past
four. Seems a fair bet the murderer used the BMW to get
away."

"Widens the field of suspects, and lends weight to the idea
it wasn't premeditated. I must say, I find the idea of anybody
planning a murder and not providing the means to get the
hell out of it as fast as possible very hard to take." Mayo
tapped his teeth reflectively. "Any results on the tyre-tracks?"

"They've taken casts, and promised to get a move on with
the results. Oh, and Terry Wharton . . . You were right, he
does have form. Seems he nearly killed a bloke once; there
was a row with a mate he was working with, and he upped
and hit him with a spanner. Lucky it wasn't manslaughter.

Four years with remission, and while he was inside he took O and A levels."

"And got himself accepted for college when he came out?"

"Some of these universities are very liberal," Kite said.

Mayo pushed his tray aside. "You've had a busy morning, lad."

"There's more. Wait till you hear this. It looks like there's a boy-friend in Mrs. Lethbridge's life—a bloke I met this morning at the house, journalist by the name of Matt Royston." The name didn't have the effect Kite had hoped, so he repeated it. "Matthew Royston. *The* Matthew Royston. 'News at Ten.' "

"My God," said Mayo, "that's all we need."

"Maybe it's not so bad. He's been taking time off from journalism, to collaborate in writing a book with Lethbridge, and he's no intention, or interest, in getting involved with covering the murder. Or so he says."

Mayo regarded this with even more scepticism than Kite, his opinion of the press in general not being very high, though he took care to keep his relationships with them as amicable as possible, working on a tit-for-tat basis: information on his side, discretion on theirs.

"That's probably where she was yesterday afternoon. I'll tell you what, though, he's in a sweat about a file of his that's gone missing. It's not in the house nor, according to Waring's secretary, at the Birmingham office."

"What was in it?"

"Notes for this book of his, as far as I can gather."

The telephone on the desk rang, and Mayo reached for it, pushing across the desk to Kite the path lab transcripts of the bloodstained papers on which Lethbridge's head had been resting. "Yes, put him on."

Kite skimmed through the reports while Mayo spoke. The document Lethbridge had apparently been working on when he was killed seemed to be the rough draft of a letter, in answer to one from a firm of merchant bankers in the City of London, called MacAllister Associates. It was signed with a large scrawl which after some difficulty it was possible to identify with the name of the chairman and chief executive, printed at the head of the letter, Leonard M. G. MacAllister. The letter comprised two sheets of A4, closely typed and long-winded. Boiled down, it came to the fact that MacAllister Associates would in the main be happy to consider giving Clive Lethbridge the backing he needed for his projected conversion of Brome House into a suite of prestige offices, with weekend conference facilities included, in return for a controlling interest in the public liability company thus formed.

Mayo, whose conversation with Waring had been brief, put the receiver back thoughtfully and waited until Kite had finished his reading. "That was Waring—he wants to talk to us. I've arranged to be at his Birmingham office at three o'clock. You'd better come with me." He looked at his watch. "Whereabouts can we get hold of this Royston? I think we should see him as well. Can we fit him in before then?"

"He said he'd be working this afternoon, back at the hotel where he's living at the moment. The Brandon Hall; it's on our way."

In the car Mayo brought Kite up to date on the interview with Dymond. "So," he concluded. "You've read the path reports—that letter seems to confirm what Dymond believed Lethbridge was hoping to do with Brome House."

"Think he's our man, then?" asked Kite.

"I'm not sure I'd go as far as that, not yet. He has pretty strong views on what he thinks of as Lethbridge's vandalism, but I wouldn't like to bet on anything with him, except that I doubt he'd ever do anything without thinking it through first. And this doesn't have the smell of that sort of killing to me."

"Maybe he didn't intend to kill, just seized his chance."

Mayo thought of that secret, contained face. Dymond was a man who would do anything for his wife, and he had hated Lethbridge, who had put paid to the plans for his wife's last years. But Mayo was uneasy with the theory on several

counts. "If he went back to Brome House in the afternoon
and killed Lethbridge, it would have been with deliberate
intent, I'd swear it. He'd have had every move planned, including how he was going to get away quickly afterwards.
Which means that he'd have had to know that Lethbridge
would be alone. And if so, we'd better find another theory for
the disappearance of the BMW. Besides, he has an alibi, if he
and Waring spoke together at four-thirty."

"Assuming he rang from home. He could have rung from
somewhere nearer to Brome House."

"And the cup of tea he took his wife at four?"

"If he did take her one. Which you seem to doubt," Kite
said, warming to the theory.

"A spot of misplaced loyalty on Mrs. Dymond's part."

"He could have walked up through the valley, killed Lethbridge, got away in Lethbridge's car, stopped to ring Waring
to establish an alibi . . ."

"Or even rung from the house—he's cool enough. But he
couldn't have dumped the car very far away in that case . . .
Doc Ison called to see Mrs. Dymond on his way home from
here, and he confirms that Dymond was at home then." Mayo
was silent, lost in thought. "It's a theory, but there's not a
shred of evidence to support it. We've got to do better than
that, Martin."

The receptionist at the Brandon Hall hotel, a magisterial
middle-aged lady, who was also the owner, was inclined to
raise objections when Mayo asked for Matt Royston's room
number, refusing with some justification to give it. She
quickly gave way, however, when Mayo produced his identi-
fication, ushering them out with some speed, as though their
presence might contaminate any guest who might happen to
come along. "His room's in the annexe. You can go through
the hotel, but it's quicker to go outside and through the car
park."

Following her directions, they made their way towards a
separate building stretching at right angles to the main hotel.

Mayo paused before pushing open the annexe door. "Take a look at that. Direct access to the car park. Easy as falling off a log to slip out of here without being seen. How long would it take to get from here to Brome and back?"

"Not too long. Half an hour, including time to kill Lethbridge."

They found Matt Royston working in shirt sleeves amidst a welter of papers that overflowed from the small writing desk on to the bed. He began to clear a velvet-covered tub armchair, apologising for the clutter. "Don't bother," Mayo said, looking at the size of the chair. "I take it there's somewhere where we can go and talk? Later we may want to go through your things. You've no objection to your room being searched, of course? Just routine."

"Would it matter if I had?"

"You could always refuse," Mayo replied blandly.

Matt laughed shortly and led the two policemen back through the reception area. The hotel had been converted from a large early-nineteenth-century house and still retained a romantic if gloomy grotto, complete with dripping rocks, pools and forests of ferns, built on to the north-facing side of the house. Even with central heating installed, it could be piercingly cold on sunless days; today, warm as it was, it held a welcome coolness, and had the added advantage, at this time of day, with lunch in progress, of being practically deserted. A couple of businessmen, expansive at the coffee and brandy stage, cigars well alight, were far enough away not to bother them.

Mayo waved aside the suggestion of drinks, and when they were seated on a comfortably cushioned cane settee, Matt on a similar chair opposite, he remarked, "It can't be very convenient, working here, can it?"

"No, but more so than trekking up from London every time I wanted to consult Lethbridge."

"Fair enough." He need waste no time coming to the point with Royston. He was a professional like himself and understood the necessity for obtaining information in the most direct way possible. He, too, was a trained observer, and those level grey eyes wouldn't miss anything much, nor that sharp intelligence fail to digest it. But he was not an impartial observer in this case, and it would be as well to remember that. And that the easy, laconic manner could well be a cover for a certain ruthlessness. Mayo understood and respected this. When the occasion demanded it, he could be ruthless himself. He found himself liking Royston more than he had expected.

"Okay, this book you were working on, now. What sort of book was it? Tell me about it, will you? I'm not altogether quite clear."

Matt explained, succinctly, a lifetime of cutting his prose to the bone standing him in good stead. The book was concerned with the major innovative British architects of the present century, those who had broken new ground, and their influence upon present-day architecture, with at least one of their major buildings, its inspiration, inception and final realisation, discussed in fine detail whenever possible—an analysis of the whole creative process, in fact. Lethbridge's own prizewinning scheme is to be the last in the book, and he'd agreed to make all his notes, sketches and plans available, charting its progress from beginning to end.

Mayo listened intently, without interrupting.

"Was he that brilliant?"

Matt took his time about answering. "To be honest, he was only fair most of the time, but occasionally he was outstanding. This Centre, for instance, was beyond anything he'd ever done; it was so innovative there was some doubt as to whether it could in fact be built at all . . . You know about it, you've seen the model?"

"I've seen it," Mayo said, "smashed into a thousand pieces."

"Smashed? God." There was a silence, punctuated by the steady drip, drip of water from the rocks into one of the little stone basins of the grotto, and the tiny throb of the pump which worked the flow. Matt fished a battered pack of cigarettes from his pocket, holding it out to Mayo, who shook his head. "You're right," Matt said, putting it back. "I've had those five in there for over a week. No point in spoiling the record now."

"Let's get back to this file of yours that's missing. Why is it so important? Don't you have a copy?"

"Sure I've a copy. I'm just bloody furious at the idea of a nearly completed manuscript of mine sculling around, for anyone to get their hands on. But it's not only my manuscript; Lethbridge's notes are with it. I've been trying to get in touch with Miss Johnson, his secretary who's just left, to see if she's any idea where it might be, but she's a very elusive lady. So elusive that nobody, but nobody, seems to have a clue as to her whereabouts, past or present. And that, Chief Inspector, is something I'm beginning to find highly suspicious."

"Are you? Why?"

Matt recounted his visit to Amanda Bradford, and what he had learned about Sylvia Johnson. "It looks to me as if she infiltrated herself very nicely into that job, and left for America, where she couldn't be contacted, very conveniently. Though just because Mrs. Lethbridge left her at Terminal Three doesn't mean to say she actually boarded the plane for Boston."

"She did, though," said Mayo.

"What?"

"Sylvia Johnson was a passenger on board the twelve-fifty flight 746 on Thursday the fifteenth to Boston. We already had that checked out by eleven last night."

Matt leaned back in his chair. "One up to you!"

"We'd have to have a bit more to go on anyway before suspecting her of murder. What could her motive have been, for instance?"

"I'm not saying she killed Lethbridge. But maybe she was planted there to suss something out for the person who did."

"Your manuscript, for instance?" Mayo remarked dryly.

"Don't be snide, Chief Inspector. It's a damned good manuscript; it just happens to be very much on my mind because I

can't finish it—not as it was originally planned, anyway—
without Lethbridge's notes."

Mayo had a feeling they may be getting away from the
point—that Royston's concern about a missing manuscript
could be a cover-up, an implication that he'd hardly be so
bothered about such a trivial occurrence if he had murder on
his conscience.

Matt said suddenly, "There was a party last week, to celebrate Clive winning the award."

"I've heard something about it already. Let's hear your ver-
sion."

Matt described the party, briefly. "I had an undefined but
very strong feeling of something wrong. Nothing I could put
a finger on, but I think Harry Waring was aware of it as well.
I've been away for a week, and he asked to see me when I
came back, but he changed his mind and said it didn't matter,
now Clive was dead."

"That's interesting. What do you think made him say
that?"

"I think he suspected Clive was up to something. He'd
been trying—Clive, I mean—to put pressure on Caroline,
about Brome, you know. She's been offered a permanent, full-
time editorial job by the publisher she reads for. It would
possibly mean living in London for most of the time. She was
worried that if she accepted, Clive might have tried to use
Pippa as a lever."

"The child to live with her, in return for permission to
convert Brome House?"

"So you know about that? Yes, well, it was something of the
sort."

"You're remarkably conversant with Mrs. Lethbridge's affairs," Mayo said bluntly. "How well do you know her?"
Their eyes met.

"I'm hoping to know her a great deal better very soon,"
Matt answered steadily, but shortly. He wasn't such a fool as
to think by admitting this he was telling the detective any-

thing he didn't already know, or suspect, or would find out, but he wasn't going to give away more than he had to.

"She was with you here, yesterday afternoon?"

After a pause, Matt said, "Yes."

"She didn't tell us that, when we questioned her. Might that have been because she didn't want to alert us to the fact that you had both motive and opportunity to put her husband out of the way?"

"She panicked, that's all. God, you don't really think that Caroline . . . !" Matt stopped abruptly. "There's been nothing between us, nothing like that. We've hardly been alone. Even yesterday, we met in reception and came in here for tea; and there were witnesses—the waiter, and another resident, an old lady with a poodle."

"And the reason for your meeting?"

"Conti, the publisher she reads for, was wanting her to make up her mind about the job, and she wanted my advice. There was nothing more to it than that."

But when they'd gone, Matt remembered that he'd said to her, "I'll think of something we can do." Her troubles hadn't seemed to him beyond what could soon be put right.

She'd replied, unexpectedly, "I don't go in much for compromise, you know," and he was reminded of how he'd warned himself not to underestimate her.

"Compromise was hardly what I had in mind—but he mustn't be allowed to trample over you—over anyone. Never fear, we'll sort him."

He'd forced himself to speak mildly, but he knew his expression was grim when he'd seen that, for a moment, Caroline had been just a little afraid.

He went back to his room and poured himself a stiff scotch from the bottle he kept there, annoyed to find how much he needed it. Taking a deep gulp, he leaned back, tipping his chair dangerously, his hands thrust deep into his pockets, jingling a fistful of loose change—and felt a small alien shape amongst the coins. The badge Amanda Bradford had given him, which he had forgotten about until now. Turning it round, he examined it more closely. The initials of which it appeared to be composed were twisted together into a circular, vaguely art nouveau-ish ornament of the kind derived from Celtic forms. The letters may have been A, M or W, encircled by a C, but in any case conveyed nothing to him. He tossed it up several times as he finished his drink, then, making a decision, reached for his jacket and made for the car-park.

# CHAPTER 12

The shop was seedy, no doubt suffering from its situation alongside the new ring road, where no cars could stop and few would bother to park and return for the poor selection of goods to be seen through the mud-splashed windows of V. Aikerman, high-class jeweller. The tarnished gilded sign above the shop seemed founded on hope rather than fact, since the goods in the window consisted of cheap watches, imitation jewellery and a depressing display of china and glass giftware. Felt-penned notices stuck on a glazed door fortified with a stout metal grating, not so much a safeguard as a prop to self-esteem, proclaimed: "Best prices for old gold" and "Ears pierced while U wait."

Matt grinned and not too hopefully pushed the door open, the last try in Lavenstock. Summoned by the ring of the bell, a small man as depressed-looking as his stock emerged, shirt sleeves rolled up and running his tongue round his teeth. A strong smell of hamburger followed him from the back premises.

"What can I do for you, squire?"

Matt, putting aside his aversion equally to the form of address and the smell of onion breathed in his face, leaned forward to place the badge on the counter, but before he could open his mouth, the other exclaimed, "Strewth, not again! What you do with 'em, eh?"

Bingo! Matt hid his jubilation with a non-committal shrug.

"You should send them back, why don't you? Them pins was never put on right in the first place. Costing you more to keep having 'em mended than they're worth. Okay, about a fortnight." He reached for a receipt pad.

"Hold on," Matt began. "I don't want it repaired; it's not mine, in fact. I'm only trying to trace the owner."

"What for?" The shopkeeper eyed him suspiciously. "Not worth the trouble, thing like this."

"Well, as a matter of fact, it's the lady herself I'm hoping to trace." Matt, whose success had often depended on his quick summing up of a character, assumed what he hoped was a meaningful expression, and was rewarded when the man behind the counter gave an unexpected cackle.

"That so? Well, I'll tell you something, squire—and for free —you're wasting your time on that lot of Jesus freaks; you'll get no joy from any of them wenches up there. Very clannish, they are, if you get my meaning."

"I thought it was some sort of religious society."

"What's that got to do with it? They're the worst of the lot, they are, all brown rice and free love, no husbands and no bras. Okay for some, I suppose, but not the sort of birds you or I'd fancy. Hari Krishnas or summat I reckon; put you off your dinner, they would."

"Live around here, do they?" Matt asked, not attempting to sort out this somewhat confused philosophy.

"Not far off, up at Branxmore. Taken over them houses that are still left up on Amelia Road, they have. Only till the council pulls them down to build some more flats, I reckon. D'you want this mending, or not?"

"No, I'll take it with me, but thanks for your information, Mr.—Aikerman?"

"S'right."

Money changed hands, and as Matt went towards the door, Aikerman called, "Good luck, squire, you're going to need it."

Amelia Road was on the very edge of what was left of Victorian Lavenstock. Its right-hand side had given place to blocks of flats, not unpleasing in appearance, a big improvement on the left side, where most of the houses had already suffered the mayhem and mutilation of the bulldozer, and obscenely indestructible polythene flapped greyly over heaps of fenced-in builder's rubble and the reeking remains of a bonfire. Sodden crisp packets and lolly wrappers impaled themselves against the sagging chain-link. Behind it used beer cans and rusty petrol tins lay where they had been tossed; an old vinyl-covered armchair sprawled with its springs and stuffing wantonly exposed.

Less than a dozen of the original houses were still standing, largish, three-storey red brick, of the more restrained type of early Victorian. Agreeable houses in their heyday, the last bastions of a more graceful age, they held possibilities even yet, though given the fate of the opposite side of the road, little hope of surviving to prove it. The short front gardens were denuded of flowers and bounded by untrimmed hedges.

The paintwork at number twenty-five, like that of all the houses, was greyish and peeling. Here someone had planted a few Michaelmas daisies, but they didn't look enthusiastic about it. Walking up the steps, Matt saw a small ceramic plaque, decorated with a replica of the intertwined initials on the badge in his pocket, and beneath it the legend: "Church of the Assembly of Alternative Witnesses."

Some privacy from the road had been provided by untidy net curtains on sagging wires, and he thought he had probably been observed walking up the steps by the speed with which the door was opened after his ring. The girl answering the door was a surprise on all counts. For a start, she was pretty, damn pretty, and was wearing provocatively tight jeans and china doll make-up. Her abundant dark red hair tumbled deliciously round her shoulders in a mass of shining waves, reminiscent of some forties starlet. She had clear, green, almond-shaped eyes, like those of a cat. He felt he'd seen her a thousand times, advertising toothpaste, or shampoo, or After Eight mints. "Hi!" she said. "Can I help you?" Her smile was slow and ravishing.

Speedily adjusting his preconceived ideas, and deciding sober caution was the watchword with this one, he rejected various interesting responses to her question. "I'm enquiring," he said, "about Miss Sylvia Johnson. I believe she used to live here?"

The girl's expression changed only in one degree, in a slight, almost illusory flicker of the green eyes.

"Sylvia? Oh yes, she did live here, but she's left. She's gone to America, lucky thing."

"I know. And it's really her address there I want. Do you happen to have it?"

"Not at my fingertips. What do you want it for?"

"She may know the whereabouts of some property of mine."

"Now look here—"

"I'm not suggesting anything untoward, Miss—"

"Morrow, Elaine to my friends. I should hope not, but, well . . . Look, you must see I can't go giving people's addresses away to strangers. It's more than my job's worth."

"Your job? You mean you work here? You're not one of the community, then?"

"Do I look as though I am?" asked Miss Morrow, arranging herself more attractively against the doorpost.

He had to admit that she didn't. As a personification of the religious life, she defied preconceptions. She was evidently not sworn to poverty, unlikely to chastity either, and hopefully not to obedience. "Come on," he said, "I'm sure you could get me that address. Perhaps we could go inside and I'll explain why I want it."

"That wouldn't be terribly convenient at the moment." She threw a quick glance over her shoulder into what appeared to be a bare hallway, with a floor of coloured Minton tiles. "And anyway, I'm pretty sure she didn't leave an address. If she wants anybody to know where she is, she'll write, won't she? What have you lost, anyway?"

He saw no point in going into detailed explanations, so he merely told her that a file of his containing his notes had been lost, and he wanted to track Sylvia to see if she knew of its whereabouts.

She listened with no show of impatience, watching him

indeed with a look of secret enjoyment, evidently nothing loath to extend her conversation with him. "I'll tell you what," she said when he'd finished, fluttering long, patently false, eyelashes at him, "if *I* had a gorgeous man like you looking for me, I'd be wild if nobody helped you to find me." Once again, she cast a glance backwards, but if it was meant to imply nervousness, it singularly failed. "He'd kill me if he knew—but, I like you, so—"

"Who?" Matt intervened. "Who'd kill you?"

But she merely smiled and continued. "If she does happen to have left an address, it'll be in the office." She pointed towards a building at the end of the road.

"The church?"

"Sure. It belongs to the Assembly. It's where all the records are kept. So just you leave it with me, and I'll see what I can do, all right?"

There was nothing he could do but accept her offer. He thanked her and handed her his card and left, with no very great hope that she'd remember to do anything at all. Or would she? he wondered.

It was a rum set-up there, whichever way you looked at it. He'd have given much to get inside the house, or more preferably the church, and find out more of this so-called sect, and what its aims were. What were they doing employing outside help, which he'd have sworn didn't come cheap? Come to that, what was a girl like Elaine Morrow doing working for an outfit like that, unless she was religiously committed, which unlikely contingency he wouldn't be prepared to bet on? All right, jobs were scarce, but with her looks she could surely do better than that. There had been something in that young woman's amazing green eyes that told him she was neither as ingenuous nor as disinterested as she might have made believe, either.

# CHAPTER 13

Harry Waring had had a busy morning.

In the next room the police had been turning Clive's office upside down, while in his own blandly tasteful private office the bright sun, filtered through champagne net, had fallen on to the rosy face and corpulent figure of Harry Waring, being unusually brisk. Mrs. Endicott, pressed but not one to hang about doing nothing, had, besides getting on with some routine work and dealing with the police—not to mention that time-wasting telephone call from Matthew Royston—trotted between the outer office and the inner sanctum with files, obtained telephone numbers direct for her employer so that they shouldn't go through the switchboard records, and then retreated discreetly into her own office. Harry thought she hadn't noticed anything odd about his morning's work, or that she wouldn't know why, anyway. She had, and she did.

By one o'clock her employer had relaxed and was looking his usual expansive self when he broke for what he considered a couple of well-deserved gin and tonics and a good lunch, indicating he'd be glad if she could stay on. Mrs. Endicott tidied up his office, emptied his overflowing waste basket into the incinerator, took out her cottage cheese and crispbread and sat back in her typing chair to reflect, resignedly abandoning the visit she'd planned for that afternoon to a Stately Home. It didn't take her long to come to the conclusion that what the C.I.D. didn't know, they wouldn't worry about. She was a widow, not far off retiring on a comfortable pension, and she saw no point in putting her job in jeopardy at this stage.

Osnabruck Road was a pleasant street of early-nineteenth-century houses, now for the most part offices, occupied by professional people—quantity surveyors, architects, solicitors and the like. The offices of Waring & Lethbridge were superior, commanding a corner position, and were carefully decorated in period style, as white as a wedding cake, the upper windows decorated with lacy wrought-iron balconies. Drawing boards and anglepoise lamps could, however, be seen through the downstairs windows. Inside there were too many people and not enough room. The light couldn't always be good enough for working.

Waring's private office was upstairs, and into this Mrs. Endicott, a small and neat, smiling, yet formidable lady with smoothly arranged steely hair, admitted the chief inspector and his sergeant. This, unlike the rooms downstairs, was not the office of a working architect, more like a sitting room which happened to be equipped with a desk, designed to give an impression of efficiency so unobtrusive that it was invisible. Though not over-large, the room was gracefully proportioned, the panelled walls painted a soft Georgian green picked out in white; velvet curtains were in deeper green, and armchairs covered in muted floral pinks and greens stood on a mushroom-pink velvet pile carpet. There were several good watercolours framed in gold on the walls.

Waring obviously liked comfort. His handshake was warm and flabby.

The chief inspector and his sergeant sat back in well-sprung armchairs facing him across the shining expanse of a mahogany desk, while Mrs. Endicott poured Earl Grey from a silver pot into rose-patterned Wedgwood china cups.

"Thank you, Milly. See we're not disturbed, won't you?"

Mrs. Endicott nodded acquiescence and offered Shrewsbury biscuits before leaving them.

Waring sat back and sipped his tea and, when the door had closed, said, "I expect you're wondering why I wanted to see you, Chief Inspector."

On the contrary, Mayo thought he had a pretty good idea

of what was to come. A confession of some sort, though
hardly to murder. Waring, unless Mrs. Endicott and the rest
of the staff, and Marcus Dymond, too, were lying in their
teeth, had a cast-iron alibi. He looked, however, like a man
who had slept on his original statement and decided that hon-
esty was the most expedient policy. Why the delay? Ten to
one he'd been up to some fancy footwork somewhere along
the line, and had needed time to cover his tracks before enquiries into the murder led to suspicions in other directions.
Nothing too black. Waring, he would guess, was too careful
of himself to risk anything much deeper than a pale shade of
grey . . . But now he had nothing to hide, he could not afford anything but sweet co-operation.

"Chief Inspector, I've been thinking about what I said to
you yesterday, and wondering if maybe I gave the wrong
impression."

Dear oh dear, thought Mayo. "In what connection?" he
asked neutrally.

"About those anonymous letters. Clive never showed them
to me, as I told you. I knew he'd been getting them, and some
nasty telephone calls, too. He once took one when I was with
him here in the office, and I suppose he felt he had to explain
—to a point. When I told you I didn't know the contents of
the letters, that was true. But—thinking about it . . . I'll be
honest with you and tell you I also had one myself." Relief
shining on his face at having got that off his chest, he allowed
himself a hasty sip of tea. "I suppose you'll think it rather
reprehensible of me not to have told you about it last night."

"We're not paid to make moral judgements, Mr. Waring,
we're paid to get the facts, and hope they add up to the truth,
but it certainly helps if people are frank with us. As a matter
of interest, why weren't you?"

Waring spread his hands wide. "I just couldn't see my letter
—or even Clive's for that matter—could have anything at all
to do with the murder. After all, blackmailers don't usually
kill off their victims, do they?"

"Blackmail? I thought you said they were threatening letters."

"What else is blackmail? Threatening exposure if you don't pay up."

Kite cleared his throat. Mayo said shortly, "We're wasting time, Mr. Waring. Blackmail presupposes something to hide. What was it?"

"I don't actually *know*. Clive was very cagey, and the letter I had wasn't specific—"

"It's too much to hope that you've kept it?"

Waring was regretful. "Ought to have done, I suppose. But the damn thing was so offensive—implying I knew what Clive had been up to, and that I could persuade him to cough up in order to have it covered up. Chucked it on the fire. Sorry about that."

"Well, it's a pity, but never mind that now. You say you don't actually know what the threats were all about. But I take it you can make an educated guess?"

Waring dabbed at a biscuit crumb on his plate and transferred it to his mouth. "I may well be wrong."

"Let's take a chance on that, shall we?" said Mayo, drawing on his patience.

"Reading between the lines, I think that somebody was hinting there was something—well, not quite all above-board about this splendid design of Clive's—you no doubt know of it, the Svensen Centre, the one that won the prize?"

"Yes, I do. What kind of irregularity?"

"I'm guessing," answered Waring after a pause. "But the accusation seemed to me to be implying that Clive had been seeing someone all right so that he'd be assured of the prize."

"You mean that he'd been using bribery."

Waring looked pained. "Well, yes. But I can assure you allegations of that sort were totally unjustified. One of the unsuccessful candidates just slinging mud, was what I thought. Nevertheless, mud sticks. If anything like that got out, it wouldn't do the firm much good."

"Was it in that connection you wanted to see Matt Royston?"

"Oh, so he mentioned that, did he?" Waring said, guileless, but not enough. So this, after due reflection, was why he'd decided to come clean? "Yes, it was. I was beginning to think the idea of this proposed book wasn't very sound, in view of those letters. Whoever was blackmailing him didn't know Clive very well. He wasn't a man to submit to threats of any kind—he'd simply have brazened it out. It certainly wouldn't have stopped him going ahead with the book—and the result would have done nothing but bring notoriety to everyone concerned. Royston was involved in writing the book with Clive, and I thought he had a right to know about the accusations. He might not have wanted to go along in the circumstances."

"What made you change your mind?"

"Simply because the whole thing's no longer relevant. I assume the book will be abandoned—or at least Clive's part in it."

Mayo let this unjustified assumption pass, and changed gear. "What did you think of this proposed scheme for the conversion of Brome House?"

"More tea, Chief Inspector—Sergeant?" Kite brought his cup over to the desk, hoping the pale liquid would be stronger now that it had stood. It wasn't, but Mayo, too, accepted another cup. Waring said eventually, "I was against it. It called for an investment from the firm I wasn't prepared to go along with. Besides, the whole idea's unpalatable to me."

"Was that why your partner was negotiating with MacAllister Associates?"

This time, Waring's astonishment was genuine. He looked blankly at Mayo as he produced a copy of the letter, and read it through carefully when it was handed to him, obviously struggling with his feelings. When he'd finished, he passed the document back. "I knew nothing of this, nothing at all."

"I understand Mrs. Lethbridge is the owner of Brome

House. This letter seems to indicate she might have agreed to the conversion."

"Caroline? Not a chance! But this was just the sort of thing Clive was wont to do, you know. He'd go ahead with something he'd put his mind to, and then bulldoze everyone into agreeing with him. I should think he'd overstepped the mark in this case."

Mayo said, "You told me yesterday you'd no knowledge of anybody who might have had a grudge against your partner. In view of what you've just told me, I'd like a list of all your ex-employees, please. The number of your staff must be relatively small, so I don't suppose it'll be too difficult, unless you have a very large turnover."

"On the contrary, we've a loyal staff, who stay with us because we pay good rates, but *none* of them—oh, very well, Mrs. Endicott will know." He spoke into the intercom on his desk. The crisp reply came audibly into the office.

"Certainly I can do that, Mr. Waring. How far back do you wish me to go?"

Waring raised his eyebrows at Mayo, who said, "Five years should do, for a start."

"Including all the temps?" enquired the secretary. "We do employ quite a few from time to time."

"Only permanent staff for the time being—we may need the others later."

"No problem. I'll be as quick as I can."

A small silence fell while they waited, which Waring, staring out of the window, broke. "This is going to mean the end of Waring & Lethbridge, you know, Chief Inspector."

"It is? And that's something you mind very much?"

"In a way, yes. My father's firm originally, you know. But in another way, frankly, no. I'd been thinking about pulling out anyway, since my wife died. I'm fifty-eight and there's a lot I haven't done yet . . . daughter in Canada, and grandchildren I've never seen. And to be honest, I haven't liked the way things were going in the firm recently—this damnfool conversion scheme of Clive's, for one thing."

So there'd been disagreements—and that news about the MacAllister negotiations had come as an unpleasant shock. Mayo speculated on the nature of their partnership clause. If Waring had tied himself up contractually to the firm for X number of years, say, and Lethbridge hadn't agreed to him breaking the contract, that could have provided more resentment. Almost certainly, Waring hadn't killed his partner, but equally certainly, he wasn't sorry to have him removed, either.

At that moment Mrs. Endicott came in and left a neatly typed list on the desk, not a long one, about twenty-five names, and beside each, the date of their departure and a small note giving the reasons for it. Most of those who'd left seemed to be women, for domestic reasons was how Mrs. Endicott phrased this. Of the five men, two had retired, one had gone to the architect's department of a local council, another as chief draughtsman to a firm of speculative builders.

Mayo's finger stopped beside the fifth name, one minus any accompanying comment. "This one? What happened to him?" He turned the paper round so that Waring could see.

"Murfitt," read Waring, "Donald Murfitt. Murfitt, Murfitt? I remember the name, but who the hell was he?" He sat thinking for a moment, frowning, then his face cleared. "Yes, I do remember him now, a draughtsman—not a very satisfactory type, as I recall. God yes, I do remember now! Clive sacked him—work not up to scratch or something. Do you think he could have anything to do with the letters?"

"Anything's possible," said Mayo. "The question is, where can we find him now?"

"Mrs. Endicott will help," Waring said with confidence, but before he could summon that long-suffering lady again, Mayo told him that he would speak to her on his way out.

"I've really no idea at all where he is now, Chief Inspector. Nor do I know why he left. He went in a hurry, but I was never told why."

"Mr. Waring thinks Mr. Lethbridge dismissed him for unsatisfactory work."

"Then maybe he did, though it would surprise me. He was generally very competent, though I have to say, really rather an odd person. He did used to infuriate Mr. Lethbridge, I remember, because he was an extremely poor timekeeper. Invariably late, and always one of the first to leave, though he only lived in Moseley. A distinct clash of personalities there, if you understand me."

"Do you have the address where he lived in Moseley?"

"I could get it for you, but I don't think it would do you much good." She hesitated. "There was nothing exactly *wrong* with him, you know—but, well, I wasn't entirely surprised to hear that shortly after he left here, he packed up and went off to join one of those peculiar sects."

"A religious sect?"

She nodded. "One of those crackpot religions . . . brought over from California or somewhere, I suppose. Like the Moonies, you know." Mrs. Endicott was herself very High Church.

"You don't happen to know its name?"

"I'm sorry, I don't—but I think they were based somewhere over in Lavenstock."

"Lavenstock?" Mayo stood up and held out his hand. "You've been most helpful, Mrs. Endicott. There can't be all that many religious sects in Lavenstock, so I don't expect we shall have much trouble in tracing it."

# CHAPTER 14

In fact, Mayo had a pretty fair idea where to look. "That odd lot of bods up at Branxmore," he asked Kite as they drove back towards Lavenstock. "What the devil was their name?"

"The Assembly of the Latter-Day Prophets? The Gathering of God?" Kite being facetious again, but the name was probably something equally meaningless, or they wouldn't both have forgotten it so easily.

The assorted members of the community had been harmless enough, as Mayo remembered them, if way-out by his own standards. A handful of earnest seekers after truth, some ageing remnants of flower power and the Me generation still finding themselves, one or two bone idle layabouts, plus a small minority on the lunatic side of extreme religious belief. An eye had been kept on them since, however. You never knew: these sorts of groups were a magnet for the oddballs and misfits of society.

"I don't recall meeting any Donald Murfitt when we were there," Kite said.

"Doesn't ring a bell with me, either."

But it had been Atkins' case mainly, one quickly over because the missing teenager, Mayo recalled, had returned home, penitent and disillusioned with the so-called freedom she had found in London, before there'd been need to question all the members of whatever it was they called themselves.

It began to rain as they left first the concrete canyons of the developed city centre behind them, then the polyglot areas of the inner city, the Asian shops and Irish banks and Chinese takeaways, where bus tickets and fish-and-chip papers and inexplicable drifts of polystyrene packing beads blew along the pavements. Perhaps the Indian summer was over. Now the windscreen wipers flicked steadily and the tyres hissed on the wet roads with barbered verges of the more affluent suburbs and occasional villages which stretched between here and Lavenstock. Kite glanced at Mayo, sitting silently beside him in the steamy car, and settled his length back in his own seat, relaxing at the wheel, Mayo's concentrated absorption telling him his attempts at conversation weren't likely to be appreciated.

Within half an hour Kite was parking the car at the end of Amelia Road in Branxmore. The rain had lessened to a mere drizzle, but it was a miserable end to the afternoon. Mayo stepped out, hunching his shoulders, and began walking towards the church, which he had an idea was the headquarters of the sect. A sombre red-brick edifice standing at the end of the road, with a low roof sloping down over its windows, like a scowl. The tall figure of a man was leaving it, striding towards the block of new flats at the corner, a figure that Mayo didn't for the moment recognise. Then he realised the man was Matt Royston. Without making a conscious decision, he set off at a sprint.

Matt, bending to put his key in the lock of his Renault, heard pounding footsteps rounding the corner. Before he could straighten, he felt a heavy hand on his shoulder. In a quick reflex action he spun round, and recognition came only just in time to save his fist from making contact with the jaw of the chief inspector. "Hell's teeth!" he muttered, feeling a fool, letting his hand fall limply to his side. "I thought I was being mugged." It took him only a moment, however, to size up the situation. "Well, well, so you didn't find my theory so cock-eyed, on reflection?" He could after all only conclude that the chief inspector had been more open to suggestion than he, Matt, had given him credit for, and that they had arrived at the same destination by different routes.

"What are you talking about?"

"Don't tell me you're not here looking for Sylvia Johnson as well."

Mayo fixed Matt with a steady look, showing none of the sudden alertness he felt. "We'd better talk, but somewhere else if we don't want to attract an audience. This may take some time." Already a window cleaner, setting up his ladders despite the drizzle, and two mothers with prams and plastic-macked toddlers, were showing a decided interest in the proceedings. Mayo jerked his head, and Kite, who had arrived only a few steps behind Mayo, led the way back towards the C.I.D. car.

The sergeant opened the back door for Matt whilst Mayo walked round to the other side and slid into the seat beside him. "Now then, you were saying. About Sylvia Johnson."

Kite, in the front seat, gave them a quick glance, then took out his notebook.

Matt pulled the broken badge from his pocket and held it out on the palm of his hand. "Ever seen one of these before?"

Mayo looked at it without attempting to touch it. He recognised it immediately as the logo of the Church of the Assembly of Alternative Witnesses. The name came back to him in full, without even trying. Kite hadn't been so far out after all. "Where did you get that?"

"It belonged to Sylvia Johnson. Amanda Bradford gave it to me when I saw her this morning. I'd forgotten all about it until after you left this afternoon."

"Forgotten?"

"Completely, I'm afraid, until I came across it amongst my small change."

Mayo gave him a swift glance and decided to give him the benefit of the doubt. He nodded to him to continue, and listened with a sharpened attention. Matt told how he had tracked Sylvia's address down by means of the badge, and of meeting Elaine Morrow, wondering as he did so how the devil Mayo had found out that Sylvia Johnson was living here. Mayo, however, wasn't about to indicate that he'd had no idea she was, until Matt had spoken. Whether Royston had really forgotten the badge or not, his tracing it here had probably saved the C.I.D. a certain amount of leg work, so he was less inclined to tear him off a strip than he might have been for not turning it over to them. "All right, leave this with us now. Thanks for the information, but in future, leave the detecting to us, hm?"

Matt slid out of the car, walked a few steps, then turned back. "The church is locked," he said. "I've tried it."

"He's bloomin' anxious to find that file," Kite remarked suspiciously, twisting round in his seat to stare after Matt's striding figure.

"You know journalists. Like bull-terriers, they are. Never let go once they get their teeth into something."

"More like an excuse to get on to a story."

Mayo grunted. "Never mind Royston; we've more important things to occupy us, this young woman for one. Why should Royston have all the perks?"

They were doomed to disappointment. The door of number twenty-three was answered after some time by a thin, tense woman who wouldn't have been a perk for anyone. Wispy, fair hair, rimless spectacles, without joy. A tight, buttoned-up mouth that barely opened enough to admit that she was Mrs. Murfitt and her husband was not at home. No, she didn't know where he was; no, she had no idea when he'd be back. She was the type who gave nothing away, on principle. Mayo didn't waste time on her, bade her good day, and left.

"Let's have a look at the church anyway."

It had seen better days. In its prime it had served a congregation of well-heeled Victorian industrialists and their lawyers and bank managers, for whom it had largely been built. Lavenstock had grown on the foundations of its light metal industry, and its aristocracy had grown with it. They had lived in the houses making up the tree-lined roads around the church for nearly a hundred years, until the houses with their cellars and attics and their lack of central heating and garage space had come to be looked upon as anachronisms, whereupon the planners were let in to begin their wholesale destruction. Here and there in Branxmore, odd houses, in some cases whole streets, had survived and were now being gentrified and lived in again as discrimination and common sense took over. This street, this church, was not so fortunate.

A few feet of path stretched between the gate and the main door, which was led up to by a flight of steps, at the base of which were two short pillars. One was surmounted by a stone ball, complete; the companion ball on the other pillar was lying newly broken on the ground. Mayo noticed, as they walked up the path, that there were several tiles missing on the long, sloping roof, stained glass had been damaged and not repaired, but on the whole the building was in better condition than he had expected. The main door *was* locked. The two detectives began to walk round the church to the back.

"Hello there! Are you looking for someone?"

A cheerful-looking man was advancing through the churchyard towards them, walking with a limp and leaning on a stick. A man with a handsome young-old face and curly hair that was receding slightly. On one side of his jaw was a large and ugly bruise.

"A Mr. Murfitt," Kite answered. "Know where we can find him?"

"I'm Donald Murfitt. What can I do for you?"

The hand not holding the stick gripped each of theirs firmly in turn after Mayo had announced their identity and requested a little of Murfitt's time. "We shan't need to keep you very long, I daresay."

"I'm in no hurry. Anything I can do. Come along, come along."

Murfitt led them along the north side of the church, limping heavily. "Sorry about the stick, and the bedroom slippers. Had a fall the other day, down the front steps of the church. Sprained my ankle, not to mention bruising myself head to foot. I didn't do the pillar at the bottom much good, either!" His laugh rang out.

"We noticed it was broken," Kite remarked.

"Oh, did you? You're very observant—but then, I suppose you have to be. Here we are."

Mayo and his sergeant exchanged looks as they followed him. They had long since passed the stage of allowing themselves to prejudge anyone, or being surprised when people didn't fit into accepted categories, but both had subconsciously been prepared for something very different, certainly not this projection of muscular Christianity, which the man radiated from his cheerful smile right down to his old tweed jacket with its leather-patched elbows.

He pushed open a small door set into the angle between the nave and transept of the church. Following him inside, Mayo saw that they were in what he took to be the former vestry. A smell peculiar to churches everywhere pervaded it, defying description but bringing to mind old hymn books and starched surplices, a residue of incense, a general odour of sanctity remembered from long-ago days as a choirboy.

The vestry had been transformed into an office of sorts by the addition of a green metal filing cabinet, an electronic typewriter, a large desk facing a small window, a couple of chairs and an old gas fire, leaving the occupants to fit in as best they could. The first thing Murfitt did was to light the fire, so unnecessarily that Mayo wondered why he did it. Kite perched on the far edge of the desk, folding his long legs out of reach, and when Murfitt pulled out one of the chairs for Mayo and took the other himself, resting his arm along the side of the desk, they were sitting almost knee to knee.

Mayo hitched his chair back as far as he could and went straight into the subject of Lethbridge's murder, which didn't come as any surprise to Murfitt. "Heard it on the local radio this morning," he said, suitably grave. "I thought that was why you were here. You must've learned that I worked for him once."

"And left rather suddenly, with bad feeling."

"Not to put too fine a point on it, I was sacked, as you must certainly have been told." He had a rather loose-lipped mouth, now turned down at the corners. "But you're wrong —there was no bad feeling. At least, not on my part."

"Really, Mr. Murfitt? You were sacked, and felt no resentment?"

"Correction. There *is* no bad feeling, not now," the other man said, doodling on a scratch pad with heavy downward strokes. It could have been a church steeple he drew, or a dagger. He looked up, smiling with benign forgiveness. "Oh, at the time, yes, I'll admit it, I felt a bit aggrieved, but the ways of the Lord truly are mysterious." He had a faint Scottish accent, which seemed to emphasise his pompous diction. "If that hadn't happened, I shouldn't be here now, doing His work, leading His flock. We all come to God in different ways."

"Is that so? And what is this work? What exactly do you do?"

"Do?" Murfitt leaned back, and his shoulders relaxed. Despite the frankness of his admissions about his leaving Waring & Lethbridge, he was undoubtedly relieved to have the subject changed, Mayo noticed. "You could describe it as learning to love one another."

"And are you paid a salary while you learn, Mr. Murfitt?"

"A token."

"Paid by whom? Who supports you?"

Mayo prepared to hear that it was the Lord who provided, and braced himself not to wince, but Murfitt shrugged and said, "We live very simply, and all our money goes into a common pool. Those who are able to work contribute towards those who for some reason can't. And many, many people are very sympathetic to our work."

Which amounted to much the same thing as Divine Providence, Mayo thought. He said, "But you must have had some capital—to buy this church, and the houses you live in?"

Murfitt smiled. "We have a Founder. A very dear and wonderful lady, an American, who came over here and started this branch of our faith."

Mayo gave him a judicial look. "You still haven't explained what your religion is exactly, nor its philosophy."

"We have no dogma. We simply offer an alternative to all forms of organised religion. We are just what our name implies—an Assembly of Alternative Witnesses, those who have been born again into a new life. You'll be surprised to learn we number former Buddhists, Jews, Hindus and even one Chinese among our followers."

With a look at Mayo's face, he added gently, "I sense your scepticism—but no one is forced to join us. We don't, Chief Inspector, entice children away from their parents, or milk people of their money, or anything at all like that. As for our philosophy—we are dedicated to Love as a principle, without commitment to any special faith. Everyone here leaves their past behind them when they come. We are all spiritually born again."

Mayo was becoming increasingly aware of a growing dislike of this very worthy young man. This was a luxury which, as a policeman, he couldn't afford. He was, however, paid for being suspicious, and suspicions were gathering fast in his mind: paramount, that he was listening to the biggest load of old codswallop he'd heard in many a long year, and that this man was getting paid for uttering such, and probably for little else. Unless, he wondered briefly, the organisation could possibly be a cover-up for something else. He'd get Atkins on to that, but he thought not. He thought it much more likely that Murfitt had simply settled for an effortless way of getting a living, a soft option that cost him nothing but the trouble of keeping his tongue firmly in his cheek. Possibly the loyalty of his followers stemmed from a similar willing suspension of disbelief.

Or maybe Murfitt, who in real life had been a nonentity, had simply found himself a role, and maybe his own suspicions were unworthy. Maybe. On the other hand, his instincts were invariably sound. He looked up and caught his sense of outrage reflected on Kite's face and felt justified.

"How long was Miss Sylvia Johnson with you?" he asked abruptly.

Murfitt's reply came glibly, as if he'd prepared it. "Two years. Sylvia was with us from the beginning, when she came here with her aunt, our Founder. We shall miss her sadly; she was one of our most dedicated members."

"Quite a coincidence, her, too, going to work for Clive Lethbridge, wasn't it?"

"In a way. To tell you the truth, I tried to dissuade her from taking the job. He wasn't a man I felt it desirable to associate with, but it was only to be for a short time, and the salary was excellent. We are prepared to swallow our pride for the general good, and what had gone had gone."

Was this what was called turning the other cheek? He would have been prepared to swear that Murfitt still harboured a load of resentment against Clive Lethbridge, understandably so. Getting the chop so summarily was something even a born-again Christian might find hard to forgive. It was at that point that Mayo had a sudden, unshakable conviction that Murfitt was the anonymous letter writer. He had a grievance, had possibly at one time had access to some knowledge about Lethbridge and his alleged corruption. Mayo was convinced Murfitt was the type who could and would bide his time and wait for the opportunity for revenge. This could well have come with the winning of the competition by Lethbridge, bringing with it a golden opportunity to discredit him in a spectacular way. But as for killing Lethbridge . . . that was a different proposition entirely. Why should Murfitt cut off the potential source of a very profitable little income? Unless he had found out too late that he had misjudged his victim and that there was no way that Lethbridge was ever going to pay out blackmail money. And that he himself could be in danger if Lethbridge chose to expose his threats.

"Well, if that's all, Chief Inspector—?" Murfitt looked at his watch.

"I'm afraid it isn't, not by a long chalk. I've quite a few

questions I want to ask yet. Miss Johnson, I understand, has gone to stay with an aunt in the States—would she be the same aunt you spoke of, the one who is your founder?"

"Yes, that's right. Mrs. Carlene Winthrop." It was an unsolicited offer which came just a little too readily, a little too pat, offered with the nervousness of a man who has something to hide.

"And perhaps also you wouldn't mind telling me why you were dismissed by Clive Lethbridge?"

Bending to pick up the biro which slipped off the desk, Murfitt made a clumsy movement which caused his bandaged foot to come into contact with the table leg. An exclamation escaped him, and when he straightened, his face was screwed up, tight with pain. "Must learn to be more careful," he muttered.

"Well, Mr. Murfitt? I asked you a question."

"Oh—yes. Didn't they tell you why?"

"I'm asking you."

"Why I lost my job? I'm sorry to say, it was too petty for words, pure spite on Lethbridge's part. A complete nonsense because I came in late once or twice in the mornings. Anyone else might have taken him to an industrial tribunal for unfair dismissal, but it would have been against all my principles to have argued over it, as well he knew. Dismissing me for such a triviality was just an excuse because my face didn't fit."

"And there was nothing else? No other reason?"

"No. Why? Should there have been?" He was on the defensive again, palpably nervous. His cheery bonhomie had slipped from his grasp. That the poor timekeeping was simply an excuse for dismissal, Mayo was inclined to believe, but the real reason? He'd known too much. Possibly he'd even tried a spot of blackmail then.

"You're a trained architectural draughtsman, Mr. Murfitt. Presumably you know of this award recently given to Lethbridge? What did you think of that?"

Murfitt took his time in answering and Mayo let him, watching him carefully. Murfitt, however, didn't even blink.

"It was controversial, but I believe it was worthy of the prize."

Mayo nodded, and left it. Murfitt's feelings on that subject would certainly be worth pursuing, but perhaps not now. He told him he would like Sergeant Kite to take a specimen of the typeface on the machine in the corner. "Be my guest," Murfitt said, easily.

"And a specimen of your handwriting, please."

Murfitt reached for a scratch pad, wrote his name and address, handed it over with a flourish. Unless he was a fool, which Mayo didn't think he was, not even a well-meaning fool, he knew he had nothing to fear in that direction. "But is one allowed to ask what all this is about?" he asked.

"It's about murder. Clive Lethbridge has been murdered, in case you'd forgotten. And apropos of that—what were you doing yesterday afternoon?"

Murfitt closed his eyes, briefly, as if in prayer. Then opening them and fixing them on Mayo, he said, "I feel your suspicions, Chief Inspector. Are you suggesting *I* murdered him?"

"Someone did," Mayo said dryly. "Someone sent a series of blackmailing letters to him and then, because he refused to pay up, went to his house and killed him."

"I wasn't that person, and I may say, your accusations are unworthy."

"Oh, I'm accusing you of nothing—yet. I'm merely asking, where were you yesterday afternoon?"

Murfitt was sweating now, perhaps because of the heat in the room, and the hand holding the biro wasn't altogether steady, but there was no panic in his voice. "As a matter of fact," he began, "as a matter of fact, I was here, in the church."

"Alone?"

"I was meditating. You should try it sometime, towards the salvation of the soul."

"I'll take your word for it, but you'd have been wiser to have had someone with you."

Mayo became aware of a welcome draught and saw that

Kite, who had been listening to all this with incredulity, had turned towards a door, presumably opening into the body of the church, which had been quietly opened. A young woman was standing watching them. How long she had been there was anybody's guess. She moved forward with a sinuous movement that reminded Mayo of a cat. Elaine Morrow, Miss World herself. From Matt Royston's eloquent description, she could be no one else. The room, already overpowering, became suddenly charged. "Tell them, Donald, why don't you? After all, the police must hear worse things every day of the week, and I'm sure they won't tell Isobel." She laughed, and Murfitt looked as though his collar had suddenly become too tight. "As a matter of fact, *I* was with Donald. Meditating," she added reflectively. Her eyes, clear and green, were sparkling; a feline smile curved her lips. She evidently liked making an entrance, enjoyed an audience.

Murfitt's hand went to the bruise on the side of his face; he licked his loose lips and gave a barely preceptible nod of acquiescence. As an alibi, it was so flimsy, it might well be true. There's an explanation for everything, Mayo thought. Murfitt's wife had looked as though she could enjoy making his life a misery. No wonder he looked scared out of his wits.

The electronic typewriter with which Kite had been fiddling in the corner, trying to make it start, suddenly whirred into life. "Oh goodness," exclaimed Miss Morrow, "what *are* you doing?"

"Not coping very well," Kite said. "I'm not used to these electronic things, only the steam kind."

"Let me show you."

Sitting down on Kite's vacated seat in front of the machine, she rapidly and expertly produced a piece of copy, which she handed to Kite. As he read it through, his eyebrows raised and he grinned. She smiled back. "There you are! I'm not just a pretty face, Sergeant."

Kite spread his hands in acknowledgement, and now that the theatrical pantomime was over, Mayo stood up. "Just one more thing, Mr. Murfitt. What kind of car do you drive?"

"I don't. From social awareness, and also because the money I should spend on maintaining one can be put to better use."

"Very admirable sentiments; wish I could afford them. We shall have to see you again, sir, so keep us informed of your movements. Don't go further than you have to, without letting us know." Kite handed Murfitt the Lavenstock Division number, written on a page torn from his notebook, snapped the elastic band back. "Good day to you."

"May God bless you."

Outside in the car, Kite rolled the window down. "Phew! With a combination of those two, we need fresh air. What do you make of all that? He wrote the letters all right, didn't he? No wonder he was sweating on the top line. Easy to see why he was sacked . . . He found the skeleton in the cupboard— about Lethbridge and the bribery, I mean. I'll get on to that."

"Let's shelve that for a while," Mayo said, to Kite's surprise. "We can't do anything until Monday morning anyway." The idea of influencing what must surely have been a panel of international judges sounded improbable. He had a distinct feeling that Waring was grinding some axe of his own there. "All the same, I think we're basically on the right lines —dig out the dirt on the blackmail, and we'll have our motive for the murder."

"Always assuming they're connected."

For a moment Mayo looked uncertain, then his jaw set. "They are. I know they damn well are. It's just that we can't see how at the moment."

Kite was silent. "Well, what now?"

Mayo looked at his watch. "Back to the office for an hour's paper work, then shove off home to catch up with some sleep. I suggest you do the same."

Kite would go home to his semi and, while Sheila got on with her housework, put his two kids to bed, or maybe vice-versa; there was no telling these days. He'd go home himself, to the flat. A drink, a meal, some music—and Julie. The last thought warmed him like a double whisky.

As Kite was about to start up the car, Mayo asked, "By the way, what was that the delectable Miss Morrow typed?"

Kite extracted the sheet of paper from his pocket book and began, aloud: " 'When I consider how my light is spent . . .' " He finished: " 'They also serve who only stand and wait'," grinned and handed it over to Travis. Fourteen lines of Milton, with no mistakes in the impeccable typing and no reason to think there were any in the text. "As the lady said, 'not just a pretty face.' And not exactly an unprejudiced witness, either—if they *are* having it off."

"If?"

"All that's a load of baloney," Kite asserted confidently. "They didn't even like each other."

"What's that got to do with anything?" asked Mayo.

Sifting through the day's information took Kite and himself a further hour and a half. So far, the tyre marks in the lane didn't fit any car belonging to anyone so far involved in the case, and no one admitted to any vehicle having been parked there . . .

"What do you think of this?" Kite passed over the details of the search of the lane running alongside Brome House, and the woods beyond. A bicycle, not new but in too good a condition to warrant the assumption of it having been abandoned, had been found in some bushes by the stream at the bottom. Well concealed, according to the man who had found it. "It's being checked out, but nothing's come of it as yet. Are you thinking what I'm thinking?"

"You think the killer cycled as far as the stream, hid the bike ready for his return, but took his chance to get away quick when he saw the BMW? It's a thought. Looking like a butcher's apprentice, he wouldn't want to risk being seen any more than he had to."

"Which clears friend Murfitt," Kite said. "He couldn't ride

a bike with that leg of his—and the limp seems genuine. It fairly creased him when he knocked it."

"I once knew a chap with a stiff leg rode a bike," Mayo said absently. "And I suppose Murfitt could have hurt his ankle *after* the murder. I'll feel happier with the theory when the BMW turns up. Hope to God it won't be long." The protective polythene seat covers the garage used while repairing cars had been left on, according to the mechanics. Nevertheless, there would almost certainly be traces, of blood at least, left behind. If the murderer had used it. If . . .

He yawned hugely and saw Kite looking as immensely weary as he himself felt. "Time for your Horlicks by the look of you, lad. Let's pack it in until tomorrow."

# CHAPTER 15

"Hi, Dad!" Julie called.

A mouth-watering smell wafted from the kitchen. Mayo's daughter was sixteen, and when she had her A levels, she would be leaving him for a catering course in Birmingham, and a flat shared with two other girls. He didn't want to spoil things for her, or burden her with the knowledge of how much he would miss her, so he joked that her going would give him a chance to lose weight: he ate like a king when she was experimenting with her cooking. But he avoided as much as possible thinking about the time when she wouldn't be here, her presence a reassurance that not everything in his life had gone sour.

When Lynne died, Julie had elected to stay with him rather than be taken into the bosom of her Aunt Laura's large and boisterous family, a joy he couldn't believe he deserved, and ought to thank God every day on his knees for. He'd been so damned scared that Lynne's sister would be proved right, that neither he nor his career would be equal to the demands of looking after a fifteen-year-old, as Julie had been then, and he'd been more afraid than ever he'd let on to Laura of all the female teenage emotional traumas to come.

But Julie had always been a sensible child, and the last two years, thank God, had brought few problems. She was remarkably well balanced. Physically resembling her mother, heart-breakingly so at times in her slender fairness, she had inherited something of his own phlegmatic nature. Not often down in the dumps, but not, he sometimes thought with a grim sense of having missed out, often on the heights, either. Lynne had had enough of that for both of them.

Life hadn't always been easy with Lynne, and they'd had
more than their share of disagreements, now bitterly regretted, about the amount of time given to his work, but God
help him, he had loved her. His only other regret, now that
she was dead, was that he had never told her how much, yet
another dimension of guilt laid on him.

Julie had made what she said was a cassoulet, with pork and
haricot beans and plenty of garlic, and bits of duck, and he
decided to open a bottle of claret.

"Wow, what's this then, are we celebrating, or drowning
some secret sorrow?"

"A dish like this deserves better than a glass of beer to go
with it."

He had avoided a direct answer, but he knew she wouldn't
press him. It had always been an unwritten family law that
unless he broached the subject of the case he was working on,
which was rare indeed, no one else should. "Cheers, love!"

"Cheers, Dad. Only a glass for me, otherwise I'll never get
through my homework."

"I daresay I can manage the rest on my own. Not going out
tonight, then?"

He was relieved when she said she wasn't, and not only
because it meant he wouldn't have to turn out again to ferry
her there or back from wherever. It was something he
couldn't get used to, the fact that she was old enough to have
her own life, though she obeyed his injunctions about being
brought home on time and letting him know where she was.
She might pooh-pooh the arrangements he had with the
Brownlows, the married couple downstairs, to keep an eye
out for her when he wasn't able to be home at nights, but she
respected it, perhaps an admission that he, more than most,
had reason to know what might happen if she wasn't careful.

They chatted about this and that while they ate their meal.
He told her about Kite's wife's good news, which pleased
Julie no end. They were all alike, today's women, supporting
each other in this new sisterhood they had. Or maybe they
talked about it more nowadays. As they cleared up, he was

reminded of Alex's transfer, and told Julie what he'd heard. "You remember Alex Jones?"

"Of course I remember her!" Julie's face had lit up, hearing the name. "She was so super when Mum died, wasn't she?"

Ashamed, he had to admit he'd almost forgotten that, as he'd pushed to the back of his mind much of what had happened in those dark days. Alex had been at school with Lynne, and they'd kept up the friendship, not all that close, but steady and continuing. Yet he recalled now casseroles left in the oven, the fridge being kept unobtrusively stocked up . . . Julie being taken out of the house to the pictures or somewhere from time to time. He was very much afraid that he had never remembered even to thank Alex. The need over, she had left them alone, and he'd never even noticed that she'd gone.

Yet she wasn't that sort of woman, not the sort you didn't notice. A real smasher, in fact, the sort who turned heads, even in the anonymity of a uniform. He decided he'd have to find some way of making a tacit apology for his boorishness.

The domestic chores over, he settled himself down with his notes and the rest of the claret, with the record player set at a restful volume.

"I'll go straight to bed when I've finished, so I won't disturb you," Julie said, kissing him good night.

"Good night, love."

He sat staring into the gas fire with its simulated leaping coals, a pale reflection of the real thing, an anodyne substitute, but adequate, trouble-free and sensible. Like his present lifestyle. Comfort in a botle of claret, the "Laudate Dominum" on the turntable, the serene mezzo-soprano voice rising and falling, climaxing, dying. Sublime, unbearable. Emotion at second hand. Mayo got up and changed Mozart for Mahler, extracted his file of notes from his briefcase and shook off his moment of self-pity.

At first he read quickly, then again more thoroughly, going through every piece of evidence connected with the case with the concentrated patience that had earned him his reputation.

Rain pattered on the window outside, Lavenstock went on with its supper and watched "Dynasty" on TV. He picked up Lethbridge's large foolscap-size desk diary and, starting at the beginning of the year, began to work through the closely covered pages.

Clive Lethbridge had had a large, confident hand, with loopy downstrokes and firmly crossed t's. Every page was full. There were notes and scribbled calculations, jostling thumbnail sketches of architectural details and fanciful doodles by the dozen, and each page held, as well as the day's appointments, memos to himself and lists of other things to be dealt with, mostly crossed off. Mayo went methodically through, from January the first, and it told him virtually nothing, apart from one interesting fact on the day before Lethbridge was killed.

The following day, the actual day of the murder, was curiously blank after all this wealth of detail. Lethbridge had particularly asked not to be disturbed on Thursday afternoon. Had that meant he was expecting someone? His blackmailer, his murderer? Murfitt? There was no appointment noted, but there were several doodles, small, rapid sketches which Mayo recognised from the photographs he'd seen as various elevations of the spectacular art gallery in the Svensen Centre.

He leaned back, overcome with amazement, and not a little admiration, at the sheer volume of writing in the closely packed, informative diary, the record of a busy life, only one of a pile going back more than fifteen years. With days and weeks, possibly months of investigation ahead, already his own paper work seemed formidable, although he did his best to keep it in check. He'd never been one for too many written notes. As far as he was concerned, they tended to fog the outline of the unique pattern that, sooner or later, every case assumed in his mind.

As yet this one was formless and shifting. The hell of it was, he had a feeling it shouldn't be. Something was eluding him, something he should have latched on to, and hadn't.

*Elimination is the essence.* The phrase sprang to his mind like a quotation. Perhaps it was.

The telephone rang.

"Deeley? Yes, what is it? Something cropped up?"

"Not exactly—well, I don't know, sir. Sorry to disturb you, sir; it's just that I've remembered."

"What have you remembered, Deeley?" He could imagine the constable, red-faced and twiddling the ends of his moustache in his embarrassment. "Spit it out."

"Those photos, sir."

Patiently, Mayo asked, "Which photos?"

"When I went with you to interview Marcus Dymond, he had some photos on the piano—school photos."

"And? Go on, just carry on from there, lad." He really didn't feel in the mood for Deeley tonight.

Deep, laboured breathing came over the line. "Sir, there was one photo there and I thought, well, they didn't *all* turn out to be blue-eyed boys. That particular bloke, for instance, got himself into some bad trouble, though I don't remember what. I couldn't put a name to him; we used to call him Brains, like in Thunderbirds—he was one of those intelligent types, you know, that wear big horn-rims, hardly knew what time of day it was, but his name came back to me now, just as I was dropping off to sleep."

"Yes? And what was it?"

"Well, I know it's not uncommon, but I thought maybe there could be some connection." There was a long pause after he had told Mayo what it was. "Sir?"

"All right, I'm still here. Was there anything else you noticed?"

"The photo looked to have been taken at a college graduation. Brains was standing with Mr. and Mrs. Dymond; must have been before she took to her wheelchair. He had his arm round her, as if he'd known them pretty well. Could there be a connection with the enquiry, do you think, sir?"

"It could be a coincidence, I suppose, but I'd think it's more than likely there's a link. All right, leave it with me, and get back to your beauty sleep. Well done, lad, and thanks. I'll see you in the morning."

Mayo stood with his hand on the receiver. What the hell did this mean? He stood, deep in thought for several minutes, then went back to his notes, to begin all over again. Back to square one. After a while, he crossed to the turntable, changed over to the Mozart again and went back to his chair, poured the last of the wine into his glass and let his mind dwell on remote possibilities and hard facts.

The facts: The boy in the photo and Sylvia Johnson shared the same surname. Sylvia had wangled the job with Lethbridge. Possibilities: If Dymond had connections with the boy, why not Sylvia, also?

Slowly, in the quiet room, a nebulous idea took shape, but the other thing that was persistently eluding him remained as fugitive as a thread of smoke.

Detective Constable Farrar, under his smooth and sharp-eyed exterior, was feeling fed-up and miserable, and mad at himself into the bargain, despite the return of the incredible weather, already hot on this Sunday morning, all on account of a two-day-old quarrel with his fiancée. They were going to be married in two months' time, and since Friday had been his afternoon off, he'd allowed himself to be taken up to Birmingham to do some shopping for their new home, an occasion which as always ended up with a tour round Rackham's furniture department. There, Sandra had seen and coveted a three-piece suite. "Oh, Keith, it's lovely! It's *exactly* the colour I've been looking for!" Jigging up and down on the settee, stroking its softness, she breathed, "Can't you just see it in our lounge?"

"Not really." Sandra was quite right when she said he wasn't colour-conscious; as for envisaging how a room might look, furnished and decorated, that was altogether beyond him.

"Try," Sandra said, sharply. "Wouldn't it look super with a gold carpet?"

He tried, without much success, but he was lukewarm, until he saw the price tag, whereupon he'd taken against the suite quite violently, reminding Sandra that they hadn't even bought the basic necessities, including a bed, yet, and that it was bad enough having half his salary earmarked for mortgage repayments, never mind shelling out the other half for cut-velvet three-piece suites that ran into four figures. Further words were exchanged, until at last Sandra had instructed him coldly to take her straight home and not to bother coming to see her again until he was in a better frame of mind.

D.C. Farrar sighed. He'd fully intended to go round that night at the usual time and apologise for flipping his lid. By that time Sandra would have come round and would admit she'd got carried away. She was a sensible girl and ready enough as a rule to concede that they couldn't afford fancy prices like that—later maybe, because he wouldn't be a D.C. all his life. But fat chance there'd been of getting off to see her in the middle of a murder enquiry. He'd been called in to the station that night and didn't get home until the small hours. Then last night when he'd called, he found Sandra had taken her dad's car and driven her mother over to visit her sister.

He felt resentful at being left out here on a limb when he ought to have been put on to some real detecting, at a loose end, waiting for nine o'clock, when he was due to continue the house-to-house with P.C. Trenchard. Nothing better occurring to him, he decided to check whether the scene-of-crime boys had missed anything in the lane where the tyre-tracks had been found. Farrar, who was keen to get on, didn't believe in leaving things to chance, or people, whoever they were, to do what they were supposed to do, without checking.

The light rain of yesterday afternoon hadn't yet obscured the tracks, though the earth around them was trodden where the men had walked to make the casts.

"Officer!"

Caught squatting on his haunches like an amateur Sherlock

Holmes, Farrar straightened up in some embarrassment as a confident, well-bred female voice accosted him. He had a feeling of recognition, but on reflection realised this was only because she was the umpteenth lady he had seen wearing green wellies and walking a golden Labrador, both of which seemed mandatory for residents of Brome.

"You *are* the police, aren't you?" Expressing a belated, if reasonable, doubt.

Farrar, who did not lack a sense of humour, made a gesture equivalent to touching his forelock. "Yes, ma'am."

"I understand you were questioning people in the village—about this dreadful happening on Friday."

"That's right. We're hoping this morning to catch those who were out yesterday."

"I wasn't at home yesterday. W.I. outing. To a micro-wave cookery demonstration. Frightfully inconvenient day, and not really my cup of tea—new technology they call it, though I call it laziness. But I'm chairman, so it's my responsibility to go, d'you see?"

"Popular outing it was; half the village ladies seemed to have gone along there with you, Mrs.—?"

"Mildmay, Virginia Mildmay, from 'Redroofs,' just along the road. I *was* at home on Friday, however. Brought Heatherington out for his usual run—and I saw a car parked here."

"You did? What time?" asked Farrar sharply, endeavouring to push away the Labrador, who, on hearing his name, had loped up and was nudging the detective with its huge golden head, and trying enthusiastically to embrace him with its filthy paws on his shoulders. Farrar backed away, fearful of his nice grey suit. The damn dog must have been in the stream in the valley, or worse. If the man existed who could patent a deodorant for wet Labradors, he would make his fortune.

"Four o'clock. Down, Heatherington!"

"You're sure of that?"

Mrs. Mildmay regarded Farrar sternly. "I *always* take him

out at four, when I'm here, just as I always take him out at eight-thirty in the morning, too. He wouldn't like it if I didn't. Anyway, Mrs. Wharton at the Lodge could confirm it. She was just by her back door, and I passed the time of day with her as I went by. Couldn't have missed seeing a car parked from there, could she?"

Farrar, following the line of her pointing finger, and noting that only a low hedge bounded the Lodge garden at the back, agreed thoughtfully that she couldn't. "Did you notice what kind of car it was?"

A little of the lady's certainty left her, but not for long. "Oh, these cars all look alike to me, but it wasn't a small car— and I do remember the colour! I've an excellent colour sense."

"Have you?" Farrar said gloomily. You and Sandra and everybody else bar me.

"Yes, indeed. And I took a particularly good look at this car. It was parked in a very slovenly manner," she added disapprovingly, "and I remember thinking old Comstock wouldn't be best pleased if he wanted to get his horse-box out. People have blocked *me* in before now, parking on my verge, picnickers down by the stream, you know." She pointed down the lane where it sloped through the woods to the valley bottom. "Until I had the staddle stones put there, that is."

Farrar knew the house now. He'd sympathised with the gardener yesterday, swearing as he tried to manoeuvre his mower between the mushroom-shaped stones. "What colour would you say this car was, Mrs. Mildmay?"

"Well now, I'd call it—aubergine. Yes. A sort of cross between a maroon and a true purple. Yes, definitely— aubergine. But what's more," she added triumphantly, "I remember the number!"

Farrar barely controlled his yelp of excitement. "The number?"

"It was a C registration, and the prefix was GOM."

"Birmingham."

"The other numbers were, let me see, a nine and an oh, and a six, I'm afraid I can't remember in what order."

"Never mind; new technology does have its uses. The computer will spit the answer out in two minutes flat. You've done marvellously, Mrs. Mildmay."

"Oh, have I? Have I really?"

Farrar assured her that she had, thanked her once more for her help, reminding her that they would need an official statement, to which she public-spiritedly agreed, whereupon they parted amicably, Mrs. Mildmay to stride off in her wellies towards the road, Farrar to intercept the chief inspector's car, which was just arriving.

Terry Wharton wasn't available for interview, having taken his two children to the Lavenstock Sports Centre for swimming lessons, but Mayo was not displeased on the whole to find Janice Wharton alone, peeling onions in the large, quiet kitchen of the big house.

"So you didn't see the car, Mrs. Wharton?"

"I may have done. We get quite a few cars parking down that lane there. They drive until the road gets too bad, then they leave their cars and walk down to the woods." Not looking at him, she swept the skins rapidly into a waste bin and began to slice the onions at an alarming rate. He took the knife gently from her. It looked sharp as a scalpel, and one fatality on their hands was quite enough.

"Sit down and let's talk this over calmly." He hitched himself on to the corner of the table. Obediently, she perched on the very edge of a straight, rush-seated chair. There was something in her submission, an obstinacy which boded the same lack of co-operation as before. Kite wanted to tell her to be careful. He was keeping a low profile this morning, himself. Already he'd had his head snapped off for no apparent reason, though Mayo was so preoccupied he was probably unaware of it, Kite thought, deciding to be charitable.

"Now, let's be sensible about this," Mayo was going on.

"It's no use prevaricating. We've a witness who waved to you from the lane, and was standing by the car at the time."

"Oh." The colour suddenly flared in Janice's face. She bit her lip. "Mrs. Mildmay. Yes, I do remember her waving now, but if I noticed the car, I've forgotten it."

"I don't think you have, you know. I think the reason you've 'forgotten' is because you knew who the car belonged to, isn't that so?"

Her head jerked up, and her frightened eyes met his.

"Who are you protecting?"

"I'm protecting nobody. I tell you I don't remember seeing a car there."

Mayo gave her a hard, bright look. "Did you think it was Mr. Dymond's?"

"Mr. Dymond's?" She appeared honestly bewildered by the suggestion. "I wouldn't have any idea what kind of car he has! He doesn't visit here regularly, not since we came. I've only ever seen the man once, and that was on Thursday morning when I let him in to see Mr. Lethbridge."

Mayo sighed. "All right, we have the car's number. It won't be long before we trace it." He waited.

The clock on the wall, a big, old-fashioned country-made affair with wooden weights and a big pendulum hanging down, clacked out the seconds noisily. "Oh God." She was suddenly shaking. "D'you mind if I smoke? I don't usually, not here in the kitchen, but—"

He did mind, strongly, with all the fanaticism of a reformed smoker, but if it would help her . . . He shrugged and gestured acquiescence. While she pulled a packet from the pocket of her overall and lit one, he signalled to Kite, who filled the kettle and plugged it in. "Coffee or tea?"

"What? Oh, coffee, please, black."

Kite found instant coffee and spooned it into three mugs.

"His name's Wisden," Janice Wharton said all at once, "The man who owns the car, Bert Wisden. He's supposed to be a car dealer, amongst other things. He's not—not a very nice type. Terry met him . . ." She broke off, her brown eyes wide, as if afraid to go on with what she'd begun.

"When he was in prison," Mayo supplied.

"Yes . . ." And she gave a kind of released sigh that was very nearly a sob, that caught the next words in her throat. "He said you were bound to find out."

"It won't be held against him—not if he's done nothing wrong."

"Try telling Terry that!"

"They never believe it." Kite placed three mugs on the table and pushed the sugar across. Mayo said nothing, and Kite, watching him stirring and stirring his coffee though he didn't take sugar, knew he wasn't hearing what he'd hoped to hear.

"What can you tell us about Wisden?"

"Not much. He came to see Terry on Thursday afternoon. Why did it have to be *then?* He said he had a proposition, a chance for Terry to make some big money. I knew it couldn't be anything straight, and I told him I didn't want him in my house. Terry was mad at me and said they'd better go and discuss it somewhere else then." She closed her eyes. "Oh God, when I knew he'd been murdered, I was so *frightened.*"

"You thought Wisden had something to do with it, and that your husband had been persuaded to lend a hand?"

"No! Yes—no, not at the bottom of me, but at first, I just didn't know. But he's sworn he hadn't, and he doesn't lie, not to me. He said he'd told Wisden to push off and get someone else to do whatever dirty work it was he'd wanted him to do, but it would be better for us to keep quiet and not mention his visit."

"Why were you frightened?" Mayo pressed.

"Like Terry said—you'd never have believed him."

"No, why were you so frightened when Lethbridge was found murdered?"

Abruptly she went to lift the lid of the Aga and threw in her half-smoked cigarette, taking her time about it. He waited until she turned round before going on. "It wasn't only because the sole alibi for your husband could only be provided by a professional villain, was it? There was another reason. You knew that Terry also had a motive for killing Lethbridge."

She stood rooted to the spot, staring at him, her eyes wide in mute appeal.

"Because the day before, Lethbridge had given you notice of dismissal."

It was Kite's turn to stare. Janice Wharton whispered, "I suppose Mrs. Lethbridge told you?"

"No." He didn't have to tell her why he knew, but he saw no reason why he shouldn't. "There happened to be a note about it in Clive Lethbridge's diary. You'd been told, the day before he died, to leave the house and job within the month, that's right? Had he found about your husband's record?"

Slowly she shook her head. "It wasn't that. They'd been having a silly argument about Terry cleaning the outside windows. Terry said that wasn't what he was paid for, and all of a sudden Mr. Lethbridge flew off the handle. He said he was fed up with Terry's attitude, and he could easily get us replaced. So Terry said okay by him, he could stuff the job." She said wryly, "You can guess the answer to that—if that was how he wanted it, he could go. It was stupid of Terry, and irresponsible, I know—but he didn't kill him, he didn't! You get hold of Bert Wisden, and he'll be able to prove Terry couldn't have. He's staying at the Prince of Wales in Lavenstock . . . Nothing but the best for him."

"Don't worry, we'll do just that." Mayo hadn't the heart to tell her that Wisden might well deny the meeting, out of spite, that he might very well take the greatest pleasure in seeing Terry Wharton in it right up to the chin. Not that it mattered all that much anyway, not now.

"All right," he said, finishing his coffee, "we'll leave it for now. Where can we find Mrs. Lethbridge?"

"Mrs. Lethbridge?" Janice blinked as if it were an enormous effort to bring her mind back. "Oh. I think she's doing some gardening. Shall I tell her you want to see her?"

"Don't bother, we'll find her."

She said, as they reached the door, *"She* knew right from the start, about Terry—Mrs. Lethbridge, I mean—but she said there was no need to tell her husband. She was prepared to help him to a new start . . . She'd never have let him sack Terry."

"But did Terry believe that?" asked Kite, as they closed the kitchen door behind them.

# CHAPTER 16

"I think I know what you want to see me about," Caroline Lethbridge greeted them soberly as they came through the arch in the yew hedge and into the walled garden, heat-enclosed on this brilliant day, October borrowed from August. She had been tidying up the roses, as if keeping up with normal tasks could deny the abnormality that had struck Brome. A trug full of late blooms lay on the stone flags near a wheelbarrow almost full of prickly stems. She drew a deep breath. "I can only say that I'm sorry I misled you."

Why couldn't anybody ever bring themselves to say, "I lied?" Moreover, she seemed to think now that she'd made this brief apology that everything was hunky-dory, that he should doff his cap and say, "Quite all right, ma'am," and that would be the end of it, when by rights he ought to give her a dressing down for obstructing the course of justice. Mayo said, brusquely, "I saw you'd changed your mind when it came to signing your statement, but we've more important things to dwell on for the moment." He almost, but not quite, regretted his tone when he saw her expression. Dammit, what right had she to shrink from him, as if he frightened her, but making him suddenly aware of his own irritability, and pulling him up short? You haven't the finesse, lad, for dealing with such tender hothouse plants, he told himself wryly. Accepting his limitations, he pressed on, however, in the only way he knew how.

"We've traced your husband's BMW," he told her, "found in the long-stay car park at Birmingham Airport."

"Birmingham Airport? For goodness' sake!"

"As good a place as any for ditching a stolen car," Kite said.

"And Mr. Royston will be glad to know his file was in it. Under the driving seat—probably slipped off the back seat."

"Well, I suppose that's very probable. Clive always brought an armful of work home on Wednesdays, for the following day, usually dumped on the back seat. Matt will be so relieved; he'll be able to meet the deadline for the book now." She pushed back the soft wing of dark hair from her face with the back of her gloved hand. Mayo noticed her pallor had been improved by judicious make-up, but her eyes still had a bruised look, their blue deepened by the dark heather colours of her simple Liberty print cotton frock. She looked as though she hadn't slept much since Friday. Well, he hadn't slept a lot, himself.

"He won't be able to have it just yet," he said. "Not until we've had a chance to examine it." Flipping through the file, he'd been inclined to regard the contents as harmless as Royston had claimed, but it would of course have to be subjected to the usual rigorous tests before he could authorise its release.

"And the car—you've been able to discover who took it—and why? Are there any indications—?" she asked, and then stopped, halted by his impassive look.

He wouldn't tell her that, of course. She couldn't expect him to. "We've not had the final results of the tests yet. It'll be in a mess. Everybody's fingerprints all over the place—but that's not what I wanted to talk to you about."

"No?"

"We need to know a bit more of the background, if you can give it, about this animosity that existed between your husband and Mr. Dymond. As I understand it, it went back much further than the sale of Oddings Cottage."

He watched her carefully, saw the surprise spring to her face, surprise and what else? Relief? A kind of guarded watchfulness, perhaps, but she answered readily enough. "Yes, that's true, they never seemed to get along, from the very beginning; I suppose they just weren't the same type. You know how it is with some people, oil and water."

"I was thinking of some more specific cause—something must have brought their dislike into the open."

"No, I don't think—" She stopped and said softly, "Of course."

She stood on the path, staring across the garden, opening and shutting the secateurs in her gloved hand, silent for so long that he was compelled to prompt her. "Mrs. Lethbridge—"

"I'm sorry," she said, blinking. "Yes, you're quite right. They were never good friends, just distantly polite to each other whenever they met, but there was nothing actually in the open—until that awful business of young Simon."

She walked a few paces along the flagged path, pulling off the gardening gloves and flapping them in her hands, until at last she stopped, looking down into the lily pool.

Mayo followed her, feeling the heat of the sun on his back, the green depths of the pool offering a grateful coolness to the eyes. It was going to be a scorcher today; he could already feel a trickle of sweat beginning to run between his shoulder blades. "Simon—?" he prompted.

"I can't really tell you much about it; I only ever knew the bare facts."

"Tell me what you do know."

She lifted her shoulders. "That Clive refused to give a job to the boy, who was a protégé of Marcus's. And the upshot of it, which was really quite terrible . . ." Her voice had become so low he had to strain to hear. "He was so shattered at not getting the job, he actually took his own life."

There was a silence while her listeners absorbed the implications of this. We're getting somewhere, thought Kite with a sudden surge of excitement, infected with the tension that he knew was building up inside the chief inspector, who looked taut, as though poised on the edge of discovery, and the effort of holding himself back was hurting him, physically.

Mayo forced himself to tread cautiously. "Wasn't that an excessive reaction, to kill yourself for not getting a job?"

"To most people it would seem so, but apparently Simon

always was—rather over the top, or so I believe. I only knew him very slightly, myself. In this instance, it was all made very much worse because Marcus accused Clive, saying it was all his fault. Clive of course claimed he'd a perfect right to refuse to employ Simon . . . Well, his actual words were that Waring & Lethbridge weren't a philanthropic society."

"Meaning what?

"Meaning, I'm afraid, that he'd reason to believe Simon was taking drugs, hard drugs, and he was in fact addicted. It was probably true. The cause of his death *was* from an overdose."

"How long ago did this happen?"

"Four or five years, at a guess."

"It would rankle with Dymond, a thing like that? He wouldn't be able to forget?"

She was very distressed. "Forget? Oh no, never that. Simon was much more than a pupil, you see. He was very close to Marcus, and Enid; in fact, he lived with them for some time after his parents were divorced. I don't believe Marcus would forget, and he'd never forgive, either, but if you're asking me if he would kill Clive for it, especially after all this time, then I'd never believe that, either."

Marcus Dymond viewed death dispassionately, a necessity viewpoint he had cultivated over the last few years, occasioned by the events that had overtaken him. Enid's painful and progressive illness he saw as one from which death would be a blessing. He believed the only pain that death itself—not its ugly preliminaries—brought was to others, and the single, solitary regret about Clive Lethbridge's demise was the sorrow it would bring to the bereaved. Even in death, Lethbridge was capable of making others suffer. He himself knew that agony intimately; he had been there already, projecting himself into the future, when Enid would leave him behind, and back into the past, when Simon had died.

He waited, watching the daily woman, Mrs. Chisholm, point the way to the two men who had rung the bell, waiting for them to reach the path to the summerhouse, the chief inspector and another policeman whom he hadn't met before, a tall, rangy man with a cheerful, youthful face.

"Enid," he began, "leave it all to me this time, won't you?"

"If you wish it, of course—but don't worry, my dear. Everything's going to be all right. There's nothing bad enough to hurt either of us."

Her calm serenity shamed him twenty times a day.

The summerhouse reminded Mayo of a Tunisian birdcage. The lacy woodwork of its octagonal frame was painted blue and white, but inside it was roomy and very English, with creaking, comfortable old basketwork furniture, and a small picnic stove. It smelled like a cricket pavilion, of dry old wood, and tea. A table was laid with cups and saucers and a teapot under a knitted cosy. The view from each side of the summerhouse was different: winding paths; a small coppice of elegant silver birch; flower beds and lawns, smooth where they faced the house; a still, natural pool. Beyond this the land dropped steeply, levelling out into ploughed fields parallel with the main road, which was far enough away not to be troublesome, before rising again to Brome House on the skyline, with Oddings Cottage in the middle distance. Church bells sounded distantly, a maple flamed against a duck-egg-blue sky, the occasional leaf fluttered to the ground, and Mayo had to make an effort not to be beguiled. He waved away the offer of one of the basket chairs which Dymond indicated, and refused tea. "Thank you, but time is pressing. Sergeant Kite and I would like to have a further word with you please, Mr. Dymond. I suggest you might prefer it to be in private."

"I've already told you all I know, and I can't see any possible reason for your questioning me further."

"That's for us to say, sir. Shall we go into the house?"

"There's nothing you can't say in front of my wife."

"I don't think you're in a position to judge that until you know what it is," Mayo insisted stolidly.

The air inside the summerhouse seemed suddenly used up.
Mayo had the feeling that Dymond knew what was coming.
He made a gesture that seemed oddly uncharacteristic of him,
a half-sketched indecisive turn, then his wife said, "Go along
with them, Marcus. I shall be quite happy here. We were
watching a heron on the pond before you came, Mr. Mayo;
perhaps he'll come back." She spoke tranquilly, and had already turned her wheelchair towards one of the windows. He
saw that the binoculars he'd used yesterday were on her knee.

"Thank you, Mrs. Dymond." He turned abruptly, to begin
the walk back to the house.

"Goodbye to you both." She was already lifting the binoculars to her eyes when they left.

Dymond showed them into the same room as before.
"When we spoke to you last," Mayo began, immediately he
was seated in that enviable armchair, "you mentioned that
your quarrel with Clive Lethbridge went back a long way.
You neglected to mention, however, the very specific event
which started it, over something—or someone—who was
very important to you, and to your wife. I'd like to know
more of the details, as much as you can remember."

"It appears to me you're already very well informed on the
subject, which I assure you can have no possible connection
with your enquiries."

"We'll be the judge of that. Please don't evade the issue,
sir."

"I can only presume you are referring to the death of Simon Johnson."

"I am."

"Which you must know I held Lethbridge directly responsible for. If he hadn't refused to employ Simon, that young
man would still be alive."

"Isn't that assuming a good deal? Most people can cope
with being turned down for a job without resorting to such
lengths."

"Most people, Chief Inspector, would not have had his
problems."

"Supposing we go back to the beginning. For a start, how you came to be personally involved with him—apart from teaching him at school, I mean."

Dymond stood with his back to the fireplace, his hands clasped behind his back, as if resigned to facing a recalcitrant fourth form with a lecture in which, if he was lucky, they would appreciate about one word in ten. "Very well." Gazing into the middle distance, he began, speaking fluently, dryly and without emotion.

"One can say of very few boys that they are a pleasure to teach, but Simon was—not only clever, but receptive. But he was a product of our so-called civilised society, of divorced parents who took off to the ends of the earth with their respective partners, his father to Bahrein, his mother back to the United States. Fortunately, they still had enough sense to realise that Simon, who was in his last year at school, needed to continue his education here, and they decided to leave him. There was a problem as to where he should live, and since we had plenty of space, it was decided he should stay here with us for a year before going on to college." Dymond paused to clear his throat. "My wife and I have never had children of our own, but Simon was—well, let's just say we had no cause to regret what we did."

"May I see the photograph you have of him?"

"How—?" Raised eyebrows, followed by cynical recognition. "Oh yes, the inestimable Deeley, I take it? One should never be surprised at anything."

"Detective Constable Deeley was observant enough to notice it, when we were last here, yes," Mayo replied curtly, annoyed by the man's unnecessary sarcasm, which was effectively quenching the thought that he might after all be human.

Dymond stepped over to the piano and, selecting the photograph which Mayo assumed to be the one that had attracted Deeley's attention, handed it over. Mayo saw a tall, good-looking boy with large, round spectacles, a defenceless face.

Mrs. Dymond looking not five, but ten years younger. Marcus Dymond looking much the same.

"Carry on, please."

"Yes. Well then, Simon had been determined to become an architect since he was a very small boy. Buildings fascinated him, and he happened to have the required difficult combination of talents—a certain artistic ability, and a complete grasp of mathematical principles. He took a preliminary course at art college, and then won a place at the Architectural Association. He was confidently expected to become a star pupil, but something went seriously wrong. Though he continued to win commendations from time to time for his outstanding work, his day-to-day progress was so erratic, in the end he left without much honour." He stopped, gazing unseeingly out of the window. "We know now, of course, that someone had already introduced him to drugs. I would like nothing better," he added, unemotionally, "than to see such persons on the end of a rope."

Poor devil, thought Mayo, exchanging glances with Kite. They knew all about those who sold misery and death to the young, the bored, the desperate. But he kept his opinions to himself. "I take it you tried to get him to accept professional help?"

"When we found out, of course we did, but there's nothing to be done if the will isn't there." Dymond contemplated the empty pipe he'd again picked up. "Naturally, he couldn't keep a job, and it became evident he was becoming more and more dependant, losing his hold. He began to look like a—a derelict. And then, quite suddenly, he seemed to find the motivation from somewhere, God knows where. He told us he'd agreed to have treatment to help him to 'kick the habit,' as he put it. Later he came to see us, and he was apparently completely cured. It seemed like—it *was*—a miracle."

"And that was when he applied for the job with Lethbridge?"

"Not then," Dymond said. "Not until he'd tried every other avenue open to him. But with his record, no formal qualifications, what could one expect? Not one person was willing to take him on, give him a new start."

"But you thought Lethbridge might have done so?"

"Not I. But Simon did. He knew someone who worked for Lethbridge, who told him of a vacancy in the firm. He was quite sure they would be prepared to take him. Simon went along, full of hope, and sure enough, he was offered the job. To say he was jubilant would be an understatement. Then a letter arrived, not confirming the offer, but curtly stating that the position had been filled. That night he took an overdose and died. It doesn't take much, as I'm sure I've no need to remind you, to push a reformed addict back over the edge." An aircraft, flying low, filled the room with its roar. Dymond waited until it had ceased. "Well, now that you have succeeded in wringing that out of me, and seen that it has nothing to do with the case, as I said, I must ask you to leave. I can't help you anymore, and I'm not sure that I want to. No doubt our present namby-pamby laws will allow whoever killed Lethbridge—if by some chance you manage to catch him—to walk free in a few years, but in this case I say good luck to him."

It was possible to feel sorry for Dymond, in the hell he'd been through, quite impossible to like him. Mayo said, apparently at random, "What happened to Simon Johnson's sister when the parents divorced?"

Dymond raised his head, and blinked. "Sylvia? Why, she finally stayed with her mother. As far as I know, she's still there. We are not, and never have been, in regular correspondence."

"She hasn't visited you recently?"

"Certainly not. Not since she was a child."

"You didn't know, then, that she had recently been employed as Clive Lethbridge's secretary?"

Dymond looked astounded. "That's preposterous! She would never have worked for that man after what he did to her brother."

"She did, however, for the last six weeks. Are you sure you didn't know?"

"I've said so. And how should I have known?"

"Perhaps she told you. Perhaps she took the job at your request. Perhaps the two of you cooked up a scheme to find some way to make Clive Lethbridge pay for what he had done to Simon. Did it start with blackmailing letters and phone calls, and end up with murder? Did it, Mr. Dymond?"

"You are talking utter rubbish!"

"I put it you that you could have walked from here on Friday afternoon to Brome House, knowing through Sylvia Johnson that Lethbridge would be alone in the house except for Mrs. Peach, who is somewhat deaf, and killed him. You could have established an alibi by telephoning Mr. Waring as if you were ringing from your own home, and then calmly walked back."

"That's neither true nor feasible, and you know it." Dymond had gone very pale, but he met Mayo's gaze without flinching. "It's pure supposition."

"Is it? It might be up to you, Mr. Dymond, to prove otherwise." He stood up, preparing to go. "By the way, what was the date of Simon Johnson's death?"

"June the fifteenth, three years ago."

"And the name of the friend who recommended him to Waring & Lethbridge?"

"Murfitt, his name was, Donald Murfitt—though he was Sylvia's friend rather than Simon's. I believe," Dymond added with some distaste, "they were both involved in some kind of freakish religion. She was, I'm afraid, that kind of girl."

"Do you mean the sort whose religious principles might state a life for a life?"

"Not at all. I mean she was just the type to take up some extreme religion. She was unfortunately rather plain, not very clever, and without even an attractive nature to compensate. Even my wife could find very little likeable about her, and I can't say that for many people."

"What sort of man is Murfitt?"

"I've never met him, only heard of him. But I thought him —misguided, to say the least, sending Simon to Lethbridge."

"Do you think it might have been through his sister's influence that Simon was persuaded to come off drugs?"

"Unlikely. He was inclined to be scathing about what he called her nutty religion, her 'do-gooding.' "

"Yet she did try to get him a job."

"That's true. She was very fond of him, and in any case, she would have considered it her duty. As I've said, whatever else, she was a very worthy sort of young woman."

# CHAPTER 17

"We're never going to make that one stick." Kite wound down the car window, letting in air that was no cooler than inside the car.

"You reckon?" Mayo still sounded somewhat short, due, had Kite known it, solely to his own inability to grasp and hold that something he still felt was there just beyond his reach. Last night he'd been gripped with that surge of tension and excitement that told him he was on the verge of a break-through, and now . . . He looked at the seat belt buckle in his hand as if wondering what it was doing there, then clicked it fastened. What he needed was time for a rethink, a reappraisal.

Loosening his tie, he relaxed suddenly. "Well, whatever, it won't do Dymond any harm to sweat for a bit. He owes us one, for Deeley if nothing else. Patronising buggers like him get on my wick. Come on, take that grin off your face and let's be having you."

They drove back to the station. Mayo spent some time in the busy incident room, where every item of information about the murder was being fed into the computer, indexed, cross-referenced. He picked up fresh information which had come in during the course of the morning. Amongst this was a preliminary report on Lethbridge's BMW, mainly to con-firm what Mayo already suspected, that the car was going to need a lot of working on. Several of the garage staff had han-dled it during the course of its servicing, leaving prints which would have to be eliminated. Hairs and clothing fibres would be more difficult, because of the protective polythene, still on the front seats. But . . . blood had been found on the driving seat covers and the carpet, quickly tested and found to be group O, Lethbridge's own, though further exhaustive tests by the experts would split it up more precisely. It was the first piece of solid evidence that had been found.

Albert George Wisden, fifty-one, of Finchley, had, it seemed, been contacted, with the result that Wharton was now apparently in the clear. A report from Deeley, who'd been sent to make the enquiry, stated that after Mrs. Wharton had thrown the two men out, they had gone on to the Prince of Wales, where they could get drinks, since Wharton was staying there. The girl who served them remembered them because she was annoyed at having to open the bar up specially at that time in the afternoon, the time when Lethbridge was being murdered.

He'd just finished reading this when Kite brought in the report of the D.C. who'd talked to the waiter at the Brandon Hall. "Odell's just confirmed that the waiter at the Brandon Hall served Mrs. Lethbridge and Royston with tea at about quarter to four. There was this other witness Royston mentioned as well. She was in the grotto having tea when they had theirs, then saw Royston seeing Caroline Lethbridge off in the car park at ten past four, after they'd finished. It's unlikely she's wrong; she's an old lady living there in the hotel on her own with nothing to do but watch other folk, and she scented romance."

Mayo said, "So that's two we can cross off definitely, three if we count Mrs. Wharton, which I'm inclined to do, barring some hitherto undiscovered motive turning up, four with Caroline Lethbridge now that the employment agency have confirmed the times she gave us. But what about Royston? What about him, Martin? D'you see him as a murderer?"

Kite thought for a moment or two. "He's capable of taking decisions into his own hands, and if he saw murder as the only solution, he might not hesitate, but I'd bet he'd look for a more civilised way out first. Though there was time for him to have done it, just."

"He'd have had to get a move on, but it's just possible."

Mayo pushed his papers away. He was back on an even keel.
He never despised instinct, that other name for gut feeling or
whether or not something smelled right, but this last hour
was what it was all about as well, routine procedures, weeks
and months of patient, even boring sifting of information,
slowly piecing a case together. Police work was mostly based
on common sense and what you'd learned about human nature. You could expect a lot of reverses and disappointments,
and a few breaks, and in the end, if you were lucky, you came
up with the right answers. If not, your career could be
blighted with one of the unsolved cases. This hadn't yet happened to Mayo, but it was one of his nightmares that one day
it might. Apart from a few back-handed comments coming
your way, if you'd done your job right, nobody in the force
. . . there but for the grace of God . . . would really blame
you for it. But you would. He pushed the possibility far into
the back of his mind and went out with Kite to find somewhere cool and quiet for lunch, where they could talk, relax
and bounce a few more ideas off each other.

He couldn't have faced goulash himself on a sweltering day
like today, but Kite was doing so with every appearance of
anticipatory enjoyment. The pub they'd chosen, in a small,
otherwise undistinguished village about four miles out of
Lavenstock, was famed for its ample, tasty bar snacks, with
good reason. Mayo surveyed his own quarter pound of Ched-
dar, the warm, crusty bread, the liberal garnish, almost con-
stituting a meal in itself, with approval, drank deep of his
cool bitter and leaned back to see if there were any new pictures. The walls were lined with them, mostly painted by a
local lady who helped out in the bar, she of the generous hand
with the cheese, and some occasionally were for sale. A good
deal of her liberality appeared in the paintings, which were
colourful and exuberant and full of life. Mayo's brother-in-
law, who was the finance director in a firm specialising in
signwriting and liked to think himself an authority on art—
on most things, come to that—had pronounced them the
work of a talented amateur. And what was wrong with that?

Mayo wondered. He liked them, and had recently bought one, a Lavenstock market-day scene, and hung it in the flat in defiance of Lynne's brother, whom he was sorry he'd introduced to the White Boar.

"Great stuff, Dolly," Kite said, craning his head back towards the bar counter, indicating the goulash and raising his glass.

Dolly smiled and cocked a thumb in acknowledgement, a cheerful, opulent woman with a lot of black hair and a gipsy appearance fostered with big gold earrings and a king's ransom of chains and bracelets.

"You're very chipper today," Mayo remarked, noticing the fact for the first time.

"Every reason to be. We've got things sorted, about Sheila's new job and that. We've been having problems because it's going to mean her working nine to five, no flexi-time, fitting her hours in as and when, like now."

"That's a pity. Used to work out pretty well for you, didn't it?"

"Right, with my peculiar hours, and with Sheila's mum living in the next road. I mean, if neither of us were there, the kids could always go round to their gran—which they'd rather do than come home, in view of the way she spoils 'em rotten!" Kite grinned and took a pull at his beer. "No, really, they think the world of her and she's marvellous with them, and I don't know how we'd have managed without her. But thing is, she's been half-inclined, recently, towards selling her house and buying one of those new flats in Hinton, all fitted up and easy to run. So naturally we couldn't spoil it by telling her about Sheila's promotion."

"She'd have abandoned the idea of the new flat, you mean?" The masochism of grandmas never ceased to amaze Mayo.

"Without a second thought, I can tell you. Obviously, we didn't want any comeback about influencing her, but I didn't much like the idea of my kids left to their own devices after school. Anyway, it's worked out after all. Mother-in-law's decided she can't bear the thought of losing her garden—and between you and me, not seeing the boys so much as well—so she's decided to stay put and have a new kitchen installed where she is. Relief all round."

Rather Mrs. Temple than me, thought Mayo, the few occasions when he'd encountered Kite's children being indelibly imprinted on his mind. A right couple of young tearaways, you needed four pairs of eyes and twenty hands when they were around. He heartily endorsed Kite's misgivings about leaving those two unsupervised after school hours.

The unrelenting heat had taken most of the Sunday-morning customers outside to eat and drink and sweat in the paved garden at the back, on the British premise of taking whatever sun you could get, though it was much more pleasant here, unpretentious, stone-flagged and cool . . . and quiet. While Kite had ordered their meal at the bar, Mayo had managed to secure a secluded corner where they could talk in private. He picked up a copy of this week's *Advertiser* someone had left, but the news of Lethbridge's murder had broken too late for him to be featured for the second week running, for even the brief official handout in the "Stop Press." He commented idly on this to Kite.

After a moment or two Kite said thoughtfully, "This business of Simon Johnson. It's bound to make a difference, give us a new angle—could even provide an alternative motive for the blackmail. A threat to expose Lethbridge for what he'd done to Simon Johnson—it wouldn't have looked too good for a man in his position, would it, refusing to give a helping hand?"

Mayo shook his head. "Doubtful, to say the least. Morally, of course, you could say the way Lethbridge acted was unpardonable, but from a pragmatic point of view—well, I'm afraid there's a lot of people would agree with what he did, with some justification. Taking on somebody with problems like that isn't something most firms can afford. All right, he could have approached the whole thing in a more positive way, offered to do what he could in other directions or something of the kind, but he wasn't that sort, and he didn't. And from what we've learned of Lethbridge's character, I can't see revelations like that disturbing him too much, anyway. Especially three years later."

"People have long memories. And it *might*, as you said, account for Dymond—him and the girl, not forgetting Murfitt. They'd all good reason to hate Lethbridge."

Yes, it had been a vicious killing. A vision of the blood-spattered room, and the savagely smashed model, recurred time and again.

"Maybe Sylvia Johnson especially," Kite continued, "depending on how fond she was of her brother."

"And who was on her way to America when Lethbridge died."

"That doesn't rule her out. She *must* have been in it, some way or other," Kite averred stubbornly. He forked up the last of his goulash and settled his length in the Windsor chair.

A three-cornered plot, involving Murfitt, Sylvia Johnson—and *Dymond*? It wasn't on, it didn't ring true, those three, not to Mayo. Yet there *was* Simon Johnson. Linked to all three. "You noticed the date Simon Johnson died?" he asked. "And only a few weeks later, Murfitt was sacked."

"That's it; the connections are too obvious to ignore! It's pretty clear the girl wormed her way into the job, possibly in order to find some way of getting back at Lethbridge for what he'd done to her brother. She found something nasty in the woodshed that they could blackmail him about—this business of the judges being bought, for instance, and Bob's your uncle."

"Too pat by far. And why wait until now?"

"Because she'd been living in America, and had only just come back home."

Mayo was shifting restlessly in his seat, but suddenly he sat up straighter. "What did you say?"

"I said she'd just come back from America."

"No, you said she'd come back home."

"Same difference."

"Not from where I sit."

Mayo's face was a study. He had finally caught the slippery fact/thing which had been eluding him for two days. He stared through the flung-back lattice window, watching a dog making a pest of itself chasing between the tables and annoying the customers, and saw the case beginning to take on a new shape. He thought, it's all a matter of perception. Like that picture: one way you saw a classical black vase on a white background; adjust your perception and two female profiles faced each other.

Or put it another way. Shuffle the cards so that they began to take on different relationships to each other. And hitherto unregarded factors became the key upon which the whole crime turned. "Waring," he said softly, suddenly. "Yes, by God. What's become of Waring since he gave us all the slip?"

"Gave us all the slip?"

Kite had failed to recognise the quotation, but Mayo was too preoccupied to bother to elucidate. "What exactly did he say, when we interviewed him at his office, about the anonymous letter he said he'd received? Got your notebook?"

Kite thumbed through the pages until he came to the relevant one. "He said the letter wasn't specific but hinted at something not being all above-board about the competition for the Svensen Centre."

"And he translated this to mean Lethbridge was being accused of offering bribes?"

"Which he denied was possible, of course."

"Of course he would. There could never be any proof, any stink, because there never were any bribes. Whereas, if the truth's what I think it might be . . . Drink up; it's time we renewed our acquaintance with friend Waring."

Kite gave up. Like Dr. Watson before him, he had heard all that the master had heard but was no nearer the solution. Whereas Mayo, the superior sod, evidently had it all sewn up bar the shouting. He wouldn't have opened his trap otherwise. Kite grinned wryly and lifted philosophic eyebrows, drained his tankard and, with a glance at the families sunning themselves in the garden as they went out, and a passing regret for his lost weekend, followed him into the blanketing heat of the afternoon.

# CHAPTER 18

Addencote was seven minutes' drive the other side of Brome, and the house Harry Waring shared with his sister lay about another half a mile farther on. Its name, chased in poker-work on a varnished plaque swinging from a kind of gibbet near the gate, was "Silver Birches," though evidence of birches, silver or otherwise, there was none. Standing on a slight rise, it was a large neo-Georgian structure of rather aggressive red bricks, approached by a short tarmac drive. Ding-dong chimes sounded when the bell was pressed, and presently the door was opened by a woman, fair, fat and nearer fifty than forty, swinging a pair of sunglasses in her hand and wearing a yellow sundress that revealed too much abundant flesh, prawn-pink.

"Yes?"

She was not too pleased at having her sunbathing inter-rupted and was ready with the brush-off until she saw their warrant cards, when her manner underwent a rapid change. Funny, this nervous reaction people had to the police, even when totally innocent. They talked too much, as if aware of some secret guilt that might otherwise come to light with the mere presence of the law. She introduced herself as Cynthia Jenner and said how awful it all was, wasn't it, and poor Caroline, and that her brother was out on the terrace, they'd just finished lunch, if they'd come with her . . .

She kept it up, her heavy gold charm bracelet a jangling accompaniment, as they followed her through a wide par-quet-floored hall furnished in a curious medley of styles. A low-arched briquette fireplace was built into an end wall; an open-tread staircase rose from the centre. An enormous cut-glass chandelier, suspended from the upper regions and re-flected in the various gilt-framed mirrors with which the hall was equipped, hung so low that Kite automatically ducked his head in passing. Ye Gods! thought Mayo, remembering the bland good taste of Waring's office, and wondering whether the house belonged to his sister, or if he'd merely allowed her her head with the decorations. They emerged through a door set into an arch, opening on to a flagged ter-race furnished with a classical-style stone balustrade, Spanish flower-pots, and cushioned chairs set round a table. A swim-ming pool of dazzling turquoise blue and a hacienda-type changing room took up most of the garden.

"It's the police, Harry." As Waring, clad in leisure wear that wasn't as kind to his well-fleshed torso as was a business suit, rose to greet them from the lounger where he'd been stretched, Cynthia Jenner went on with scarcely a pause for breath, "Sorry about the clutter; if you'll excuse me, I'll just clear it . . . Would you like some lemonade? It's home-made," she offered, waving a giant insulated pitcher.

If Waring was surprised to see them, the sunglasses he wore effectively concealed it. He gave them his flabby handshake, waved them to chairs and said, smiling, "Oh, something stronger than lemonade, surely!" His own glass indicated red wine. "No? Well, we can rustle up some coffee if you like."

"Lemonade will be fine, thanks."

Cynthia poured the icy fruit juice into tall glasses and then made a great business of clearing the table of what was evi-dently the remains of lunch. Waring padded across to her on bare feet and picked up the piled tray when she'd finished, and with an adroit manoeuvre, shepherded her in front of him into the house. In a moment or two he was back, saying affably, "I assume it's only me you want to see. I'm sure you'll excuse my sister; she has things to attend to . . . people com-ing in this evening for drinks." His voice was gravely low-ered. "Caro and Clive would have been here, of course. We did think of cancelling, but life, as they say, must go on . . ."

"Quite." Caro and Clive, Mayo thought. "You saw a good deal of them, socially as well as in business, then?"

"Lord, yes. Known Caroline all her life—and always been very fond of her."

"And Lethbridge?"

"We became partners shortly after they married." Mayo noted the different shading of the response.

"A man of integrity, would you say?"

"No question." This answer came blandly, readily; the mouth smiled, the eyes were hidden behind dark glass. "But we went over all this yesterday. I fancy it isn't what you came to talk to me about."

Mayo leaned forward, lifted his lemonade glass from the table and sipped it as if it were the finest malt. "Professionally, and as far as that's possible without personal bias, what was your considered judgement on the design for the Svensen Centre?"

Waring's sunglasses might conceal his expression, but his bare feet gave him away. The toes curled sharply, involuntarily, then slowly relaxed. "The Svensen Centre? There's no other word for it, in my opinion, but spectacular."

"And didn't you find that surprising?"

Waring suddenly sat up and took off his sunspecs, reached for the packet of cigars on the table beside him, waved it questioningly at the other two and then, as they shook their heads, cut and lit one himself. "I'm not sure that I follow you," he said carefully.

Mayo said, "I'm told that Lethbridge was a good, competent architect. That he'd never designed anything on this level before."

"That doesn't mean to say he never could. We're all of us, at times, capable of expanding our reach beyond what anyone imagined of us."

Indeed, indeed, and here was Waring, capable of surprising him, but already halfway to admission. The slightest tremor of his hand as the lighter flickered showed the hesitation in his mind. Mayo waited patiently. Waring wasn't a man to hold out; he would always take the easy way. As he had before. "In that, I echo your sentiments. All the same," Mayo said, making it easier, "I believe you may have had doubts."

"Doubts? Not in the least. As I told you yesterday, there was no question of undue influence. No one in my firm has ever gone in for that sort of thing, not even pre-Poulsen." Waring gave his urbane smile, drew on his cigar and observed the glowing tip.

"I'm not talking about bribery. I'm talking about the design itself. I think you knew it wasn't Lethbridge's."

From the direction of the kitchen came the whirr of some electrical applicance, a mixer or some such, working in sporadic bursts. Waring said nothing. Neither did Mayo, letting the silence draw out until Waring would have to break it. He did so sooner than Mayo had hoped. He seemed relieved as he began to speak.

"Well," he said, "I'd hoped . . . But never mind. All right, what do you want to know?"

"The truth about the design, Mr. Waring, that's all."

The other man drew on his cigar and then said, "It wasn't the brilliance that surprised me, you know. Clive always had more potential than he realised, but he'd always seemed too intent on success to risk the failure or ridicule of stepping too far out of the mould . . . Do you understand me?" Mayo nodded, and Waring went on, "It was the style. Simply, it wasn't his. It didn't have his signature; it had none of the personal idiosyncracies and repetitive themes every architect of any pretensions at all subconsciously develops. But . . . I was out of the country for most of the time the designs were being prepared for submission, working on one of our projects in Australia—and to be frank, I didn't let it bother me too much because I thought it was in any case far too avant-garde to stand much chance in a competition of that nature. When I heard it had won, I was amazed."

"And because of the kudos it brought to the firm, you smothered any misgivings you might have had?" Waring shrugged, spread his hands, avoided looking directly at either

of them. "You must have had a shock when the blackmail
threats began to come in. That's what they were about,
weren't they? Not accusing Lethbridge of trying to influence
the judges, but of appropriating someone else's design."

"What could I do? I tackled Clive about it, and he denied it,
absolutely. I'd no alternative but to believe him." Waring's
voice was loaded with self-justification.

"Did you know, or suspect, whose the design was?"

"I had no idea, none at all."

"What does the name Simon Johnson mean to you?"

"Nothing whatsoever." The response was genuine, Mayo
would have sworn.

"An extremely talented young man who applied for a job
with your firm three years ago?"

Waring shook his head. "Is that who—?"

"Yes," Mayo said, with conviction. He stood up. "Have you
got all that, sergeant? Right, sir, we'll be on our way now.
Thank you for your co-operation."

"Just a minute," Waring said. "What's going to happen?"

"I can't tell you that. All I can say is, Simon Johnson won't
be claiming anything from you; he's dead."

Waring also got to his feet, in an ungainly scramble. His
rosy affability had abruptly gone, leaving him shaking. Vary-
ing degrees of shock and alarm chased each other across his
face as new probabilities occurred to him. "Dead? Dead,
when? You can't go yet! I've a right to know what's it all
about, surely. My God, this is more than I bargained for!"

"I'm sure it is—but I'm sorry, that's all I'm prepared to say
at the moment. If there's anything you need to know, you'll
be informed in due course. There's one thing you can tell me,
though," Mayo said as he reached the door into the hall. "Was
Sylvia Johnson American?"

Waring's frantic alarm was stilled. "Sylvia—Johnson?
Clive's secretary? *Johnson?* My God."

"Was she? American?"

"No. No—I don't know. She didn't have an American accent, not so's you'd notice."

"Thank you, Mr. Waring. Make the most of this weather; it can't last."

They left him to sweat, on the Spanish patio beside the pool, though clouds were already beginning to obscure the sun.

# CHAPTER 19

The golden morning had dulled by the late afternoon into a heavy, leaden humidity. A wind got up, blowing up for rain, but hadn't yet brought coolness. It had grown so dark that the lights had had to be switched on in the interview room, and so stuffy that all the windows were thrown wide open. Caroline and Matt, brought there by Mayo for purposes of his own, sat uncomfortably on hard chairs under the stark fluorescent lights. A stolid-looking policewoman sat in the corner, the short sleeves of her uniform shirt strained around her fat, freckled arms, her freckled nose shining with perspiration.

Mayo didn't keep them waiting overlong. He had plenty of reasons for not wanting to draw out the proceedings. He came in, followed by a man leaning on a stick, a woman and Sergeant Kite. There scarcely seemed enough air for all of them; there were too many people in the small room, seated round the centre table, with Mayo at the head—though not centre stage. The focus of attention was on the young woman, a focus drawn to herself without words, by the sheer force of her personality.

"Mrs. Lethbridge first," began Mayo, turning to her. "All I want you to do is tell me if you recognise either of these people. Take your time."

Caroline knew she'd never seen the man in her life before. Receding curly hair, petulant expression. Dejected, a superannuated, fallen boy scout. An impression reinforced by the tweed jacket with leather patches he was wearing . . . in this heat?

But the girl.

For a long time Caroline looked at her, knowing immediately and intuitively, as women often do, but needing to be absolutely sure. She was met with a defiant stare from green eyes, a toss of luxuriant coppery hair. She looked away, and the image of another girl superimposed itself on her mind. Take away thick-lensed spectacles, drab, shapeless, figure-disguising clothes, a self-effacing manner. Substitute contact lenses, skilful make-up, a new style and different colour of hair, clothes designed to draw attention. Above all, replace the habit of fading into the background with the confident projection of self . . .

Caroline turned her gaze back to the girl in front of her. "I do know her. She's Sylvia Johnson."

"Mr. Royston?"

"She told me her name was Elaine Morrow."

"Her name is Elaine Morrow, but she's the woman you knew as Sylvia Johnson, Mrs. Lethbridge," Mayo said, "and she's being held for questioning in connection with the murder of your husband."

The relationship between Murfitt and the girl was a fragile one. Not one to stand up to the pressures being put on it. Mayo knew it, and Elaine Morrow knew it, too. Mayo could see it in her face as she looked at her erstwhile—friend, lover, accomplice? The knowledge that he was going to save his own skin, whatever the cost to her.

He thought he could sense the struggle going on in her, a conflict between her innate need to dramatise herself, to tell the story in her own flamboyant way before an impressed audience, and the innate secrecy of a nature that precluded her from admitting anything. For the moment, she was refusing to answer questions, to talk at all. Mayo left her with W.P.C. Sutton, a stolid young woman who wasn't impressed by much, presently let the others go, then went to concentrate on Murfitt.

Murfitt was closeted in the small interview room with Mayo, Inspector Atkins between them like the Rock of Gibraltar, all of them wilting in the heat. His lips were stubbornly set, but his thick, pale skin was glistening with fear and perspiration.

"Why don't you take your jacket off?"

Murfitt clutched his lapels, then removed it. An acrid stench of stale sweat pervaded the room. He might have done better to leave it on, anyway. Without it, in his shirt sleeves, his confident self-image seemed to dissolve. He looked defeated, without the air of being set apart from those who could do wrong.

He licked his lips. "What'll happen to me if I tell you the truth?"

"It's more what'll happen if you don't." Mayo wasn't prepared to start trading with Murfitt. "Like being charged with being an accessory to murder."

"You can't do that!"

"Can't I?" Mayo asked nastily.

Murfitt was very badly shaken. He'd give in and admit what he knew sooner or later, sooner at any rate than Mayo's patience, endless in such situations, would give out. "She's been using you, Murfitt. Think about it."

You could see him doing just that as the questioning went on, and finally he broke at the same time as the storm, at the first clap of thunder. The words came forth just as the rain did, large, heavy drops at first, then a torrent, and afterwards relentlessly, monotonously, falling on and on.

It promised to be a very long night.

It had all seemed so simple at first, Murfitt began, an opportunity to avenge himself for that humiliating dismissal from Waring & Lethbridge. Dismissal, not for being late a few times, but because he'd stuck his neck out, feeling it his duty to inform Lethbridge what had happened when Simon Johnson had received his letter. A high moral tone entered, bolstering the self-justification. Lethbridge's rash and ill-consid-

ered promises, cruelly raising Simon's hopes only to dash
them again, had certainly sent him to his death. Clive Lethbridge was a murderer. Murder was a mortal sin. Sinners
should be given the opportunity to repent—

"Or accept the wages of sin?"

"No, no!" Murfitt's eyes rolled. He looked like a terrified
horse. "I didn't mean that!"

He meant that Lethbridge couldn't have been allowed to
remain in ignorance of the consequences of his action; he
meant that he, Donald Murfitt, had felt it his duty to inform
him of what had happened. It was only right that such a one
should feel remorse. He *deserved* to have it on his conscience . . .

Self-righteous, Lethbridge had called him. To be more precise, a bloody self-righteous hypocrite. A busy-body. And
much worse. "And what do you propose to do about it?" he
had demanded. Knowing there was nothing at all to be done,
that he would as usual ride over any accusations of moral
turpitude, merely laugh or more likely counter-attack, as he
had in actual fact done, by finding the first opportunity he
could to get rid of Murfitt. The bad timekeeping was an excuse Murfitt wasn't prepared to fight, Mrs. Carlene Winthrop
and her Assembly of Alternative Witnesses having by then
arrived timely on the scene. All this was what Murfitt said.
He mentioned nothing of the slow-burning resentment Mayo
sensed in him. Perhaps it was hidden even from himself.

"And then?"

It wasn't until two years later that Murfitt had opened his
newspaper and read the news that an international award had
been given to a local architect, and seen before him the art-
ist's impression of the group of buildings that would shortly
be the completed Svensen Centre.

He would never forget that moment of choking disbelief.
He knew those designs, intimately, and the last time he'd
seen them had been the night when Simon Johnson was getting his portfolio ready to take with him to the interview the
following day with Clive Lethbridge.

Faced with the sketches in the newspaper, hardly able to credit the direction his thoughts were taking, Murfitt poured himself a stiff glass of brandy and then went along to the reference library and looked up several of the most recent issues of magazines devoted to the interests of the architectual profession. Sure enough, he found there what he wanted, a laudatory article discussing the Svensen Centre, spread over several pages, together with photographs and detailed plans.

He sat there, staring into space, and then went home and wrote a letter to Elaine Morrow. She was on his doorstep within a few hours of receiving it.

"Tell me about Elaine Morrow. What you know about her."

Elaine, Murfitt said, was the woman with whom Simon Johnson had lived for nearly six months before he died, an influence on him as strong as the pull of the moon on the tides. She had virtually dragged him from disaster . . . though in retrospect there had always been something several degrees less than normal in the fierce, intense possessiveness she showed towards him. A power which, had Murfitt stopped to analyse it earlier, might very possibly have prevented *him* from acting as he had.

He had had no doubts that she would have kept all Simon's work, and indeed, when she arrived back in Lavenstock, she brought with her everything Simon had ever done, including the portfolio he had taken with him to the interview . . . and the Svensen Centre designs were not there. She remembered them, as clearly as Murfitt did, even though she hadn't been able to bring herself to look through Simon's work since he had died, and so hadn't noticed their absence. The conclusion they reached was that Simon, on the day of his interview, excited and euphoric at being offered the job, had accidentally overlooked them when gathering his things together before leaving Lethbridge's office.

And that Lethbridge, learning of Simon's death, hadn't bothered to return them. He'd kept them and then, certain no one was going to claim them, had made use of them.

"I'll make him pay," Elaine said. And that was when she'd contrived a friendship with Amanda Bradford in order to get nearer to her objective, to find out how she might best get her revenge, and grasped the opportunity, when Amanda left, to take her place as Clive's secretary.

And that was it, Murfitt shrugged.

Not by a long chalk it wasn't, Mayo said. "That's when it all began, when you began to blackmail Lethbridge, threatening him with exposure—making out you'd some proof the drawings weren't his. A serious crime, attempted blackmail."

"Money was never asked for! Only an admission—to see Simon get his rightful due."

"Oh, right, nothing but the purest of motives! And vengeance? Revenge? They didn't enter into it, I suppose. Give over, Murfitt."

Murfitt said at last, sulkily, "Oh, if you like."

But that was *all* he'd done, he insisted, gone along with Elaine, made a few telephone calls for her, to put the wind up Lethbridge good and proper—which they'd succeeded in doing. Elaine had been there and seen the effects of the calls Murfitt had made, the letters she herself had written. "And that's the truth." He leaned back and wiped his damp forehead; the rain drummed on the flat roof and poured down the gutters.

"Why did she pass herself off as Sylvia Johnson?" Mayo asked at this point, Murfitt evidently believing he'd come to the end of his statement.

"I don't know."

"*You don't know?* Come on, try again."

"I *don't* know. She's the sort who likes to play games. There's no telling what goes on in her mind, and no stopping her either, once she's set on course."

"Playing games in the church Friday afternoon, weren't you? Both of you?"

Dull, furious colour stained Murfitt's cheeks; a hunted look came into his eyes.

"Or were you cycling towards Brome House to keep an appointment with Lethbridge? Hiding your bike in the bushes, and leaving it there after you'd murdered him, using his own car to get away instead?"

"You're making a lot of assumptions, without any proof," Murfitt said, trying to summon some spirit.

"Except your dabs all over the bike."

"Not surprising, if, as you say, it's my bike! And aren't you forgetting something—how could I drive a car, let alone ride a bike, with my leg like this?"

His protests were token. He was backing down, now that they were getting down to the dangerous nitty-gritty. Now that suspicion was pointing its finger at him.

"Let's take it again, shall we?" Mayo asked. "Starting with Friday afternoon . . ."

# CHAPTER 20

"It's all wrapped up," Mayo said. "Elaine Morrow's been charged with wilful murder and will be committed for trial."

"She's confessed then?" asked Woman Police Sergeant Alex Jones.

"As much as she ever will. There'll be no difficulty in assembling the evidence against her, anyway. Forensic have come up with hairs and prints in the car—fibres, too, though she burned every stitch she was wearing that day, threw them on the demolition site bonfire at Amelia Road. Her plea that she killed Lethbridge under provocation's hardly likely to stand up, in view of the elaborate charade she set up beforehand."

"By that you mean her impersonation of Sylvia Johnson?"

"And the pretence of taking the flight to Boston."

They were sitting together amidst the self-consciously fashionable green and gold neo-classical decor in her sister's flat, above the shop, where Alex was staying until she found somewhere of her own to live. Mayo had been unaware that she had a sister, let alone that she was Lois Fielding, Interiors, owner of the small but expensive boutique just off the Cornmarket, here in Lavenstock. Half an hour after ringing the bell and being persuaded into coffee and ham sandwiches, he was still surprised to find himself there at all, to find that he'd so quickly taken up her invitation to drop in any time, when he and Alex had renewed their acquaintance at the station. Never before had he felt the need to discuss a case, other than with those directly involved—but then, never before had he had a case quite like this . . . and Alex, after all, was on the inside, so to speak.

She was wearing gold studs in her ears and a suede skirt with a perfectly matching striped silk blouse that reminded him of mint humbugs, but nevertheless met with his approval. Feminine, but not fussy. In uniform, she tended to appear rather prim and severe, with her pale complexion and black hair, shining and cut in a sharply defined style. Out of it, she smiled more, the vividly blue, thickly lashed eyes danced, in tune with a cheerful, optimistic outlook on life. He speculated on the possibility of a bit of Irish in her ancestry.

"So why did she do it?" she asked, extricating the coffee-pot from a table crammed with miniature obelisks, statuettes and a malachite spillholder.

"Take on Sylvia Johnson's identity? Because if Elaine, as Sylvia, came under suspicion of any kind, she'd have an alibi, since Sylvia was three thousand miles across the Atlantic when the murder occurred."

"What I meant was, how the dickens did she expect to get away with it?"

"I don't think it ever entered her head she'd be caught. She lives in a fantasy world where anything's possible if she wants it to be so. The flaws in the plan she simply shut her mind to, and maybe because failure was unthinkable to her, the whole thing might just have come off." When logic ceased, that was when the difficulties of detection began, sometimes defeating careful, inexorable step-by-step police procedures. "And you know, there was more than a sporting chance Elaine Morrow might never have come into the investigation, if she'd had the sense to take herself off back to London and disappear, immediately after the murder, instead of believing herself invulnerable."

Mayo had asked that question of himself—why hadn't she put as much distance between herself and the crime as possible? But that was before he'd begun to assess the depth of her obsession with herself and the effect she was producing. The answer emerged clearly enough during his interrogation, and was simply that she could not have borne to be absent, never to see the drama she had created unfolding.

"Is she mad, do you think?" Alex asked, following the direction of his thoughts.

"That's for the shrinks to say, not us, thank God, but I don't think so, not within the clinical definition. Unbalanced, yes. Over the top to the point of outrageousness, sure. She just has to see herself in some kind of role, in this case first as Simon's saviour, then his avenger. She's an exhibitionist, she exists at a permanent remove from reality, and I think Murfitt was right when he said to me that living on the edge of danger was necessary to her. It gives her the stimulus and the spice she needs."

And so the temptation to remain on stage had been too great, even though she must, by then, have known how perilously close she was to discovery. "What's more, if she'd gone back the way she came, by bicycle, and left Lethbridge's car alone, there'd have been precious little evidence to connect her with the case."

Why *had* she taken Lethbridge's car?

"I didn't know there'd be so much blood," she'd admitted when he questioned her about it, and he'd sensed her first and only moment of natural panic. "I was in a terrible mess, and I couldn't risk anybody seeing me. And then I saw the BMW outside the window and I thought, why not?" A sparkle in the eyes at that reckless moment remembered, giving a charge of excitement that banished any fear. "I drove back to Amelia Road, changed and then dumped the car."

About certain aspects, she had talked quite freely to him, the parts in which she thought to appear clever. Not knowing that the chief thing which invariably impressed Mayo about the criminal mind was its ultimate stupidity. But then, her whole confession had been a self-regarding presentation, her green eyes brilliant as she made it. She showed no shame, no remorse. Yet all through, she kept up the fiction that she hadn't planned to kill Lethbridge. Which perhaps indicated, after all, a subconscious admission that she was not so entirely unworried about the consequences as she made out.

"What was the reason you went to Brome House, if not with that intention?"

She shrugged. "He'd ignored the letters, the calls. He had to be made to understand there was no bluff involved. Never mind waving it aside."

"So you made an appointment to see him?"

"Appointment?" She laughed. "Why did I need an appointment? I knew he'd be there, working on his precious conversion scheme, most likely. He had probably given orders not to be disturbed—he often did on Thursdays—so I went in through the french windows. I wasn't going to give him the chance to refuse to see me. He didn't recognise me, of course."

"I'd like you to tell me exactly what happened."

"I told him who I was, and what I wanted, and he just sat there, sneering. He told me to go ahead, prosecute, try to blacken his name, whatever, he couldn't care less. There was no proof he'd stolen Simon's drawings, and he'd just deny everything if necessary, and we could do what we liked. Nobody would believe, or even care, what he'd done, he said. He didn't even bother to deny it, as if I was of so little account that my knowing about it was almost beside the point."

It was the worst insult he could have offered her; Mayo could see that. Remembering it, she seemed to metamorphose before his eyes into a different being. Her lips tightened, the face became pinched and bitter, plain, and it was possible to envisage the young woman everyone had known as Sylvia Johnson. The change was brief, a mere moment before she laughed and was again Elaine Morrow. "He said if he heard any more, he'd go to the police. He actually jerked his thumb and told me to get out the way I'd come, through the garden. And then he simply ignored me. He picked a pencil up and began writing, just as if I wasn't there. I went behind him and I picked the inkwell up and hit him. He fell forward without a sound, and I hit him again, several times, to make sure."

It wasn't, whatever she said, as spontaneous a response as

that. She must have gone prepared with some sort of weapon, but there was no way she was going to admit it. The inkwell had been there to hand, she'd used it, and it added veracity to her insistence on unpremeditation.

"And then, before you left, you smashed the model."

"The model," she said casually. "Oh yes, I smashed that. With my shoe. And then I thought perhaps I'd better muss the place up a bit, to make it look as though there'd been a break-in."

"It was much the same sort of thing," Mayo said, shifting his backside on the slippery silk of an elegant but damnably uncomfortable sofa, "as using the coincidence of Mrs. Lethbridge's appointment and actually going down to Heathrow —which she'd no need to have done. But it added authenticity, and automatically diverted suspicion from Sylvia. A bit more embroidery . . . like hinting to Caroline Lethbridge that the reason behind her going to America was that she'd fallen for Lethbridge, which might well have been the sort of thing which could happen to the real Sylvia."

"What *about* the real Sylvia Johnson?" Alex asked. "She must have known what was going on, surely."

"Apparently not. It's not inconceivable that she closed her eyes to it—she loved her brother deeply, and mightn't have been averse to a little revenge on her own part, but that's a point that might never be cleared up. She'd been staying with a friend in Brighton for the last couple of months. Elaine was in touch with her, learned her flight time and planned accordingly. All she had to do was to walk away when Mrs. Lethbridge left her, catch a train back to Lavenstock and become Elaine Morrow again, do what she had to do. I wouldn't put it past her to have arranged to see Sylvia off."

"Some people are like that, they enjoy manipulating others for the sake of it; it gives them a sense of power." An unexpected sharpness in her tone caused Mayo to look quickly at Alex, but her expression remained cool, if analytical. "After all, what she did for Simon was manipulation, of a kind."

"She called it love."

"That's not love, Gil," Alex said. "That's just an extension of the ego."

There was something off-key here, a personal intrusion that needed exploring. The chi-chi apartment wasn't conducive to thought. He tried concentrating his vision. A bust of Napoleon, brooding on top of a marble column, gave him no help.

Alex, perhaps aware by his silence that she'd revealed more than she wished, returned to the safer subject of the murder. "Wasn't it unnecessarily risky, pretending to be Simon's sister?"

"The name's common enough not to arouse suspicion, even if Lethbridge or anyone else had known Simon had had a sister. And if they had known, it wouldn't have mattered. Because that Sylvia was American, as Simon had been."

He ought to have realised this when Murfitt had mentioned the American aunt, and that Sylvia had come over with her to found the English branch of the sect. When Marcus Dymond had spoken about the parents' divorce and the mother returning to America. The fact *had* registered subconsciously, but only surfaced when Kite had spoken, in the White Boar, about Sylvia coming "home." It had sounded wrong, it was wrong. Home to Sylvia was America. No one connected with the case had mentioned her being American, for the simple reason that the Sylvia Johnson they knew wasn't. It was this that had set his mind working, pointed the way to the successful solution of the case.

Solution? What was ever solved by murder? And what was success?

He drained the last of his coffee and stood up, ready to go. Alex stood up, too. Frowning slightly, she stepped across to the fireplace and adjusted a small picture that was a fraction out of line. A thought that had been lying submerged in Mayo's consciousness chose this moment to rear its head.

Cautiously he examined it, considered it, but it was too new and untried. It involved too many assumptions, too little knowledge. About himself perhaps, mainly about Alex and, despite the cheerfully tolerant facade, the something in her that spoke of the perfectionist who might expect too much of anyone. Maybe that's why she'd never married. Perhaps not many men would care to subject themselves to the test.

He asked abruptly, "Why'd you come here, Alex?"

And was sorry he'd asked, although she smiled as she answered, and gave a reply he knew she'd prepared. "I'll tell you about it sometime. When we know each other better."

He didn't know what to think about that. He was all at once very tired of thinking at all. He felt middle-aged. A knackered, middle-aged copper—in need of a good night's sleep, he thought wryly, to clear his head and rid himself of fantasies.

"Thanks for the coffee. Good night. Until tomorrow morning." And the next case.

She smiled and touched him lightly on the arm, and suddenly he felt heartened by what she'd said. Sometime they'd know each other better. And the thought entered his mind that the day might well be worth waiting for.

# CHAPTER 21

The best view of the drive was from the room they called the library, named so because it contained marginally more books than any other room in the house, and predominantly those of the greatest dullness. At Brome, books were meant to be read, and the more interesting ones had long since been dispersed comfortably amongst most of the other rooms. One day, Caroline promised herself, one day she would catalogue them all . . .

It was a masculine room of crimsons and browns that was welcoming on a lamplit winter evening with the curtains drawn and a cheerful fire blazing in the grate. Today it was sombre, the thick, stuffy draperies and heavily patterned carpet emphasising a dull and weighty day, with dying leaves floating listlessly to earth.

Waiting for Matt's car, her bag packed, ready for the journey to Brittany to fetch Pippa home, she sat on the cushioned seat by the open window, in the aimless state that had lately characterised her.

There was so much that would have to be done, but not yet, presently, when all this was over. Now was a kind of limbo, between one life and the next, with nothing to do but think. And her thoughts sometimes frightened her. Things were never going to be the same again. A family in which murder has occurred never could be the same again. A murderer had entered and would remain as a presence among them, first companion to the victim, marked and remembered by his terrible end.

And for the first time in her life she would have to make decisions.

It seemed to Caroline now that she had moved straight from the dominion of her father to that of Clive. I shall have to learn to be myself, she thought, trembling.

The decision uppermost in her mind, needing resolution, was that involving the future of Brome. The new offices Clive had envisaged would no longer be needed now that Harry was retiring and Waring & Lethbridge would shortly cease to exist. Perhaps she and Pippa could occupy the part of the house destined for such, and the rest could be converted . . .

The irony of it did not escape her. She wondered from time to time if she had opposed the conversion plans just because they had been Clive's—looked at dispassionately and not swayed by remorse, modified to some extent, the idea might be a workable solution to her problems. Matt thought so, but she knew the decision had to be hers alone. That, at least, she could do for Clive. Accept the best of what he had left, forgive the man he'd been, smaller than he need be.

Matt's car was coming up the drive. Caroline stood up, closed the window and went outside to meet him.